Appreciating Angels

Sarah's Story

One girl's journey of self discovery
through adversity

By Sally Asling

Appreciating Angels

ISBN 978-0-9564194-3-9

A copy of this publication has been registered with the British Library. For more information, visit www. appreciatingangels.com.

Cover photo: Model, courtesy of Vizzi Photography – all rights reserved.

This title has been classified as young adult fiction; some readers may find some of the content upsetting.

BlessingsBook PUBLISHING

Published by The Blessings Book Limited in 2010

www.theblessingsbook.com

Printed by MPG Biddles Ltd, Norfolk.

Appreciating Angels

Sarah's Story

Contents

Foreward

This is a story about a girl I was privileged to meet and know. I met Sarah after embarking on the start of my spiritual journey. Sarah confided in me and shared her most amazing life journey by way of a blog. Sarah wrote her story in a blog, the detail of her past being too painful to talk about face to face. I have kept Sarah's written word exactly as she shared it.

What she told me that day changed the way I view the world, and those within it.

Like me, you too could write about a part of someone's life, or even your own life. In your story, you will be the main player and hold the leading role in your drama, as Sarah does in hers.

Just as we all have our parts to play, what is fascinating is the way in which all of our lives are interwoven. We cannot often appreciate the complexity of the weave, or the pattern on the cloth, without the benefit of hindsight.

I sometimes think about the 'walk on' parts and the 'non-speaking' parts as much as those who feature as 'co-stars' or in 'pivotal roles'. Whilst these characters' are in Sarah's life, I wonder which characters these people play in someone else's drama.

Did meeting Sarah for a few seconds, minutes, days, weeks or months have any impact at all on their lives in the way they may have impacted hers? Did meeting with her change their lives?

After all, there is no action without reaction and every reaction is echoed onwards. So for every bad deed done, is the consequence in Sarah's drama or that of someone else?

Is justice an earthly deed or a spiritual consequence?

There are those that, like me, believe that the immortal and everlasting soul becomes the human spirit for a short while. There are those that believe our earthly life is all mapped out for us, by ourselves. It is also thought that, while the soul is in its purest form before it is incarnated, we planned our time here on earth to expand our knowledge and progress our soul's journey.

There is also a belief that we even pre-choose and pre-agree to meet other souls that will help us along the way, who appear to us as angels and lead us into situations to teach us what we need to learn. If this is so, there is therefore no such thing as a chance meeting.

Whatever happens to us along our path, the universe is unfolding exactly as we preordained, and guiding us through the journey. Bringing new people, angels, into our lives who help us through a difficult period.

If you met an angel, or if you were an angel, how would you know? This book is dedicated to all the walking, talking angels out there.

Now: **The Call**

Sarah had dropped her child off at school, made herself her morning coffee and started to plough through the incoming mail in the inbox.

Sebastian, her dog, was making himself comfortable under her chair. The sound of silence was delicious after the hectic pre-school dash. Sarah typically enjoyed the first ten minutes of her working day by just organising the brain and making the transition from Mum to Businesswoman over a cup of coffee.

Life for Sarah was good. On the window sill was the vase of white roses and gypsophila her husband of sixteen years had bought her for Mothering Sunday. There was a card with a lovely verse still calling each other by their pet names and signed with "All my love. My rock, my best friend and my soul mate."

Next to this, and not to be outdone, Sarah's child had picked some buttercups and daisies and had crafted a card with a picture of a giraffe on it. It made Sarah feel content with life. Living in her Kent cottage, surrounded by countryside, she was part of a stable happy family.

From the day she met her husband, Sarah knew then she would be with him forever. On the night of their first date, on which he kept her waiting for two hours, but wait she did, Sarah later learnt his mother had passed away. The angels had put them in touch, their work was done. Knowing that his mother's last wish was that he would meet his lifelong partner had been achieved; the angels left them to it. A little late, but better late than never.

Sarah laughed out loud at the image that suddenly popped into her mind. She had agreed to the date after a few weeks of engaging conversation. On the day of her date, she had moved from her studio and had all her worldly possessions packed in a rucksack and was carrying a frying pan come wok thing that wouldn't fit in the rucksack. As she waited for him at a bus stop, she was well aware how silly she must have looked with a frying pan in hand.

Sarah was happy and content just reminiscing on these times and thinking how fortunate she now was. Looking out of the window this morning was no different to any other. The sky was that brilliant blue and the late spring leaves on the tree looked fresh and clean against the backdrop of uninterrupted blueness. It was going to be a warm early summer's day. Sarah mused that it would bring on a growth spurt of the plants in the greenhouse that were already struggling in their three inch pots. She made a mental note to dedicate herself to some re-potting later, time allowing. Trying to be self sufficient was an idealistic dedication, but she was enjoying trying nonetheless.

The rather piercing shrill of the phone interrupted these thoughts. Sarah hated the ring on this phone, so shrill and mechanical. She wondered what had happened to the good old "Brrr Brrr"?

"Good morning, thanks for calling 'Select'. This is Sarah, how may I help you?" She trilled robotically as standard, gulping the dregs of the coffee and standing up so she could project her businesswoman's voice.

"Is that Sarah Lamb?" The voice was female, soft and nervous.

"Yes, who is this?" Sarah hadn't heard her maiden name voiced for best part of ten years, possibly more?

"It's Katie. Um, Katie. Katie Stoke, you remember Katie from..."

"I remember."

There was silence. Sarah sat down, not sure precisely if her knees gave way, but she sat. She felt like she was physically and mentally being rushed through space, like a vortex, spinning like the Tardis through time and space. Flashes of lightening striking at her, stars and images shooting past taking her back to a place she once was, to a person she used to be, to a time long since locked away. Images flew through her mind, like fast photo shots. She clutched her stomach as a rise of nausea swept over her. She was suffocating, drowning.

"Sarah?" A pause. "Sarah, are you there?"

"Um.." She managed to squeak whilst taking a breath for the first time in what seemed longer than the moment it was.

Sarah could feel the cornflakes at the back of her throat mixed with coffee. She wanted to put the phone down but she couldn't. She was frozen.

"Sarah, I am sorry, I wanted to just . . ."

It was twenty-five goddamn years for heaven's sake, why the hell was she calling now. "*Twenty-Five Years*," said her unconscious mind to her.

Sarah heard a slight sob catch Katie's breath as she said, "I know, and not one of those years has gone by without me thinking about what I did and..."

Sarah interrupted, "Didn't Katie, it's what you didn't do." There was sudden anger in her voice.

"No. Sarah, no." She said letting out a long sigh. Was it of remorse or regret?

"It was me that called for help. It was me that waited until you had been taken away in the ambulance. I saw everything. I saw what they did, I . . ."

Her voice faded out. *Twenty-five years.*

Twenty. Five. Years.

Yet, on this gorgeous sunny morning Sarah sat, as a thirty-eight year old who had moved on, running a business, a mother, happily married, transported to a place she didn't want to be. She could smell the dirt. She swallowed. She could taste the blood and semen. She shut her eyes and opened them again slowly. The trees swayed gently, and one small fluffy cloud was drifting towards the oak tree. A rather pudgy magpie saw off the squirrel on the bird table.

"You watched? You saw? Yet you didn't do anything? I thought you had run off, that's what you told the police. You even denied seeing those men, you called me a liar. Katie, you called me a liar, yet you saw, you saw? I don't understand, why now, why are you calling me. How did you get my number? What do you want?"

A pause hung in the air for what seemed like a lifetime, but was only a few seconds. Sarah focused on her words.

"You never said. What did you see?"

"I noticed your profile on Facebook and tracked you through the social media sites. I knew you were in Kent, I just didn't know where. I wanted to call before but, well, it's more relevant now."

Sarah thought her voice sounded tearful. Unlike her own. Sarah had every emotion, but could feel nothing.

"It's history. It's not relevant to anything"

"It is to me" Katie's voice sounded sharp.

Sarah felt suddenly angry as she said, "It didn't bloody happen to you."

Her voice, now quiet, replied, "It may have well of done. It's crippled me for years; I've had to have counselling to deal with it, several times. I just wanted to see how you are now. It means the world to me that you are making a success of your life after the way you were. The way you were after, you know ... I didn't think you would live through it."

Shame, Sarah thought, ***poor you. You had therapy for something that didn't happen to you. You left me just when I needed you and you turned all available help open to me away because you couldn't speak out the truth.*** Sarah didn't care. What had meant so much once now meant nothing. It was too late.

"I'm sorry." Said Sarah. More silence. "I have to go. I have an appointment soon."

The clock said 9.30am. Sarah really did have an appointment at 10.00am. She had heard enough.

"Can I call you again?" Katie pleaded, "I need to tell you what I saw."

Sarah felt suddenly both curious and sad. The visualisation of what happened started to play again.

She blinked and said, slowly, "I know what you saw because it happened to me. I played it over and over. I don't want to hear about it, but if it helps you, I am here."

Sarah was not sure she meant it. She put the phone down. She didn't say goodbye. She just sat numb. Waiting. Remembering.

Silently, tears that should have been cried twenty five years ago started to fall.

Sarah's Story: 1985

I was getting ready, ahead of the night that changed my life.

I sat with Katie, Rachel, Bobby and Nina on Debbie's bed. Madonna covered her walls with her crucifix and fluorescent socks. Her songs were blaring out from Debbie's new twin-deck stereo system. Debbie was trying to get Rachel's eyeliner on, making thick black lines that looked crooked to me.

Bobby was padding her bra with cotton wool, which Katie said, felt lumpy. They were pulling it out and trying Body Form sanitary towels instead. I was sticking up my mini skirt using a stapler. I had just got it so it was in line with my crotch and my legs looked rather good.

We were planning to go into Birmingham to a nightclub. All we had talked about throughout the week was getting hold of fake ID. I was borrowing a friend of Nina's sisters ID, I was borrowing ID from a friend of Nina's sister. She too was on the heavy side and we always seemed to look older. No one really knew her so my fake ID wasn't of much interest to anyone.

I did my hair in the same style, short and very eighties with sharp sideburns and spikes on top. My ample boobs were struggling to contain themselves in the ill fitting bra and my top was mega tight and very low. I positioned it so it sat just above my nipples, with a cleavage to die for. My denim skirt was now positioned with my crotch. I thought I looked fantastic.

Nina and Debbie were in jeans and had matching denim jackets and white T-shirts. Bobby as normal was in long dark purple skirts and flowing black tops with various crystals handing from her neck. Bobby was a Goth.

Katie and Rachel, like me, were both in miniskirts and crop tops. I was too large for jeans. I was told by Mum they only did children's to a certain size and I would be a big adult. Leggings were fine anyway, I didn't really care. We had our leggings under the miniskirts but at the last minute we decided to take them off and 'show a bit of flesh'. After all, tonight we were girls on the pull!

When 'Like a Virgin' came on, we picked up the various hairbrushes and sprays as makeshift microphones and all crowded on the bed screaming, "Fucked for the very first time!" Dissolving into giggles straight after.

Debbie's Mum was away for the weekend. Her elder sister Allison was a bit of a rebel, a punk with plenty of piercings, I never asked Debbie about her Dad, it was sort of taboo. Allison burst in at that moment.

"Turn it down kids! You're putting Mickey and me off our video."

Allison too was making the most of the freedom by having Mickey round. Debbie said the night before he stayed over and she could hear them having sex.

We crowded round Debbie while she told us what she had heard. We knew nothing about sex but everyone, bar me, had now all at least snogged. Debbie had even reached second base and had let Peter stick her finger in her at the playing fields. That was the coolest thing any of us had done.

"Do you reckon they are actually at it?" Nina said.

Debbie grinned. "The bed was hitting the wall and she was calling out 'Yes, yes, yes!' So yeah, I reckon."

Katie let out a long, "Shiiiiit, she had better be being, you know, careful. Jeeez."

Debbie grinned and said there was a condom floating in the loo and said it was still there. Of course, we all rushed to look but the evidence had long gone.

It was Debbie, with Allison's help that had got us the fake ID's. Debbie swears she had got in 'Diva' the previous week with Allison.

"They didn't check my ID or nothing." She boasted, telling us about the smoky atmosphere, the cool beat and of course the BOYS! Debbie reckoned she has snogged someone deffo over 18 and that he rubbed himself up against her when they were dancing and he had gotten a hard on. She also said she had shared a cigarette with him and he was so cool he could blow smoke rings.

We all listened to Debbie holding onto her every word and dreaming that like her we could get off with someone tonight. All we had to do was pass as eighteen. We were all fifteen but it shouldn't be too hard with makeup and clothes.

We had to get the bus into 'Brum' and had put the money for a taxi home aside. I didn't like Birmingham very much, the Bullring Centre with the popular cheap clothes store 'Mark One', and its open market stalls, always seemed a little dangerous to me. Just a feeling really. I liked the art galleries though and the theatre was just the best. As for nightclubs, well, I couldn't say having never been to one before.

Just before we left Allison handed round a bottle of voddy. "Just a small one." She said. This was the best; I envied Debbie for having such a cool big sis.

Done 'up to the nines' with our lipstick, made up faces, short skirts, Impulse body spray and clip on earrings we had confidence in our stride as we bounced to the bus stop. Talking over loudly, we thought we were so grown up. Our confidence, fuelled by the Vodka, made us feel invincible, our hopes and expectations of 'getting off' with a boy (or man) was sky high.

Now: **Susannah**

Sarah confided in me that she had written to Susannah again last night by e-mail telling her that she loved her. She asked if she could ever have any feelings for another woman. Susannah replied back that she cared about her, just not in that way.

It's not the first time this discussion had taken place. It was ten months ago that Sarah wrote to her and told her that, after three years of knowing her as a friend, she had fallen in love with her.

Sarah told me that despite her revelations Susannah never once has judged her. She said that Susannah has remained understanding, considerate and a true friend.

Sarah appeared to hero worship Susannah, I asked her where this "crush like" obsession came from.

Sarah told me that for the last four years, it's been Su who had inspired her to do so much since having her child. Sarah explained that Su is a quiet lady and in quite a different class to her own. Sarah explained to me that Su oozes refinement laced with dignity; that she is perpetually calm and understanding with a huge heart. Living her life like the Desiderata. Though quiet and gentle, her spirituality being complete as she radiates a loving nurturing nature.

Over time Sarah had told her things that she had never told other people, she had talked about things never talked about before. Sarah didn't know why, she didn't really understand the connection. Sarah didn't really understand her feelings for Susannah, she said she loved her. But Love comes in all forms and Sarah was confused.

Since Sarah had taken the call from Katie, she sometimes felt really down. It brought lots of things to the surface for her, like the need to share it with me now. Sometimes, despite being close to forty, Sarah tells me she longed for someone to care for her in the way a mother would care, and certainly not in the way a husband could.

Sarah would say "Men like to fix everything. I don't need fixing, I am not broken."

Now: **The Callback**

Sarah's phone rang at 9am. She expected it though she didn't know why there was something that made her just think it would.

Sarah didn't even answer the phone properly; she simply picked up and said, "Hello."

The voice at the other end asked "Sarah?"

Sarah was not sure if she wanted to say yes.

But she did.

"Sarah, is now a good time to call you?" It wasn't. Sarah said nothing.

"Sarah I can call back. When is a good time?" Sarah didn't answer again. "Sarah you used to do this when we were friends, not answer when you were thinking. I couldn't read your mind then and I can't now. Speak to me please." She said.

"I don't know what I am meant to say Katie," Sarah responded at last. This being the truth. "Katie, I am not sure I want to revisit things so long ago now. I have moved on. I don't know how it can help you either. Are you sick?"

Sarah had to ask. It had crossed her mind that she was terminally sick and needed to get this off her chest.

"I am not sick Sarah. It's just that I still think about you."

This Sarah could understand. As life goes on, you are caught in day to day things, but sometimes things happen that trigger past experiences to surface. If the truth be told, Sarah had thought about Katie and several other people several times a year, but had moved on, the past becoming irrelevant.

"Sarah. I had counselling about a year after you were attacked. It didn't really work, but then I wasn't really truthful." Now that Sarah could relate to. Sarah was never truthful on the couch.

"I had a baby two years ago, I tore terribly. I thought of you."

"Great," thought Sarah. "Nice to know I am remembered for the good times."

"Last year my husband left me. Turns out he has feelings for someone half my age. I am pregnant now, five months and I have a weak cervix. I have to go and get stitches fairly frequently ..."

"And you thought of calling me?" Gruesome.

"Sarah, I never appreciated what really happened until I was older. My parents made me keep away from you. They blamed you for me failing my exams and having to re-sit them. By the time I got to college and I saw you, I just remember you turning your back."

"I am sorry if you expected more. I hated you, I think I still do." There. Sarah had said it. Now she could go away and get on with her cervical issues.

"Sarah ..." There was silence.

Sarah had a feeling something important was about to be said when she heard, "I am sorry." Well, nothing monumental and what was sorry all about anyway. Just words.

What Sarah then said surprised her, "Katie, you never told me how fat I was, and you never told me what the men were saying. You must have known."

Another silence. This one feeling like an eternity.

"It all seems too cruel now. We were fifteen years old Sarah. You were fat, you were our friend. We assumed you were happy."

"I was happy, Katie."

"Exactly. Everyone envied you for your personality, your laughter, your ability to attract and hold a crowd, you were great fun. To be honest we saw you, not your size."

"Did you know what the 'pork a pig' contest was?" Sarah started to have flashbacks. She was sweating and shaking the nausea rising again from within her.

"I don't know. That's the truth. It didn't seem ugly. It was just they had bets on how many could snog you. You wanted to get off. We just thought all credit to you. It seemed just fun." She said.

"They were laughing at me," Sarah started to feel sick.

"Sarah we were drunk. You were the most sober because you were snogging most the night, we were drinking so much more, and well, Sarah, I think because you were bigger you held it better anyway."

She was always the master of back handed compliments. "Did you see me go outside?"

"Yes, you seemed happy enough," she said.

"Why didn't you check to see if I was OK?"

"Sarah, you seemed set on going a little bit further."

Sarah covered her mouth thinking she was going to be sick. She sat down on the sofa and stared at the tree. It was still there. Her world was turning upside down but that oak tree that must be one hundred and thirty years old was still standing.

"Sarah, are you OK?"

Sarah's Story: **Club Diva**

Bobby and Debbie got into Diva's easily. Nina and I got asked for ID, but it worked. Katie and Rachel were told they couldn't come in. I challenged the bouncer and said we were all the same age. He clearly couldn't be bothered to argue or debate the issue and waved them through.

Darkness. My eyes blinked to get accustomed to the dim lights. There was a cloakroom for coats, but we hadn't bothered, so we went straight to the Ladies. The room was thick with smoke, really heavy. I coughed and Debbie said she thought she had forgotten her inhaler so went out. I needed to pee so Nina and I went in the same cubical, one to hold the door as the locks were busted.

"Fuck," I heard Bobby exclaim. "I've got panda eyes already."

Katie offered to help correct Bobby's make up; goodness knows how I heard with the noise of the music.

Was it music? It just seemed to be heavy booming. It was so heavy, the walls were vibrating. It hadn't seemed so loud on the outside.

We left the Ladies and went into the club, clutching onto one other excited just to be there. The under lighting on the stairs, wall to ceiling mirrors, carpet and drapes on the ceiling, the smell of stale sweat and perfumes all blended to make Diva's the height of sophistication for us.

We chose a corner close to the speakers. When I say chose, it was the only one left, probably because you had a good chance of losing your hearing that close. Debbie pulled out another bottle of voddy.

"Allison gave it to me. Well, that's the least she could do after I fished out the condom for her and said I wouldn't tell Mum."

We laughed. They had a great relationship based on bribery and threats, but it worked and we all envied her having older sisters.

I could feel the effects of the vodka. I suggested we get some OJ to dilute it a bit, which we did.

We were not really talking as we couldn't hear each other; we were just taking in the atmosphere. Couples on the dance floor were gyrating against each other, looking pretty cool. There were also loads of people snogging on the sofas and up against the wall. At the bar was a group of older lads.

"Phwoar," said Nina. "He is so fit."

We looked over. There was a guy with short hair gelled into big spikes, with another guy with a pony tail.

"Which one?" I questioned. "Surely not the girlie." Everyone laughed, which quickly muted as they came over.

"Wanna groove?" Said 'Spiky' to Nina, who looked at us but needed no encouragement.

'Ponytail' said to Debbie, "Want to know what a real man feels like?" He held his hand out and Debbie was gone.

Shocking chat up lines I thought.

I turned round to see a rather tall guy flirting with Rachel who was walking back from getting some nuts at the bar. They stopped halfway and I saw his hand shoot up her top. I started to feel a little jealous and left out. I turned to Katie who was making eyes at a black-skinned man at the bar.

"Oh Katie, no!" I exclaimed as she walked over to him.

I sat on my own for quite some time, watching all my friends in various areas of the club individually entwined with a male or dancing up close to some lad. Even though they kept coming over for a drink or to see if I was OK, I started to feel a little left out.

Then a large group of lads came in, about thirty of them. I heard them talk of a stag night. I looked at my watch. It was 11pm. The club was pretty busy now and it was getting harder to keep track of where everyone was.

A guy came and sat down next to me. "Friends dumped you?"

I smiled and said it was my turn on bag watch, pointing to the bags all around me. "Too bad," he said. "Not seen you in here before, do you come here often?"

I smiled. Whilst it was clichéd, it was also a fair question. I shook my head. "First time."

He took my hand. "I wonder what else it's your first time for?"

Before I knew it, he'd pressed his lips against mine.

OMG. My first snog! I thought.

I hoped Nina and Katie looked over. I opened my eyes and caught a glimpse of Debbie giving me the thumbs up.

He tasted of beer and smoke. He smelt a little sweaty, but I was not going to complain. I felt him grab my boobs and rub them. His mouth now pressed against mine pushing my head onto the back of the sofa, I pushed him back. I needed air. It wasn't so gentle now.

"Fuck, you are one prick tease Missy," he said. "Wait here, I'm going to get a beer." I watched him go to the bar where he was being clapped on the back by his mates who were cheering.

I looked out for Nina. She was certainly glued to the guy she was with half an hour before.

Debbie was walking back with Katie. "You OK?" They asked.

"You bet," I said.

"You seemed stuck in," Debbie laughed.

"Too right!" I said, "I want to go second base tonight and he is the one."

I don't know what propelled me to say that. I had no intention of it. Least of all with that sweat box.

"Hey Sarah. Look!" Nina said pointing to the bar. His mate was coming over.

A large guy came over and sat by me. "Paul said I would be nuts not to snog your face off." He said as he launched on me.

He was far better than Paul. His hands were not clammy as they pulled up my top and touched me. He wasn't so hard to kiss and he came up for air.

"Do you wanna come and meet the gang?" He said. I agreed and I went off with him to the bar. Again, I got the thumbs up from Debbie and Nina who were also enjoying my success.

His mates seemed drunk. Or, if not there yet, well on their way. They were chatting to me and giving me a few voddies. Every now and then one of them would pull me outside the circle to snog me. I felt amazing. I couldn't believe I was the one getting all the attention.

I noticed Katie waving at me, calling me over. I made my apologies and left the lads.

"Time to go babe," she said. "It's gone one and we had better get back."

"Just a bit longer," I said. "Come and meet the guys, they're a great crowd."

Katie agreed. Nina shouted over, "We are getting a cab back now. See you back home. If you stay, you have to make your own way back."

Katie said that we shouldn't split up. I persuaded them all to stay another half hour and for us all to meet at the entrance. Once agreed I wandered back over to the lads, enjoying their attention. Within moments of joining them, one of the lads had started to kiss me again. This guy was pretty good and whilst his hands roamed everywhere, I wasn't complaining.

I felt Katie pull my arm, "Sarah, the others are bored, we are quitting, come on."

The guy stopped kissing me and said, "I'll get you home babe," and we started kissing again.

Katie looked perplexed. "Sarah. No. Come on."

I told her to buzz off, I was OK. Annoyed at the brush off and being ignored she just said, "Fuck You!" and walked off.

I was too caught up in the moment. I didn't comprehend or care about where I was, or the dangers. The alcohol and the beat had me in a trance, and if this was what it was like to get off with someone I was hooked.

I felt his hand up my skirt, his fingers tugging at my pants. Then he pulled away and stopped kissing me. I thought I may have done something wrong, he just said, "Wait there."

He left me and walked over to the group of lads now further along the bar with hoards of pretty girls around them. Whatever he was saying was pretty funny as his mates all clapped him on the back and were laughing and high fiving.

He came back over. "Did you, erm, like that, you know, I mean what we were just doing?"

I nodded, "Yes."

He pulled me to my feet, "Let's go outside where we can be alone."

I walked with him to the door passing Katie on the way. She pointed to her watch. I grinned and mouthed "Ten minutes" as I walked arm in arm with him out of the door.

It looked like I may beat the others to second base after all.

Sarah's Story: **A Karmic Contract**

It was cold outside and I felt goose bumps cover my bare arms and legs. I shivered.

"Soon have you warmed up," the guy, I think who was called Paul said.

We walked out of the club and round the corner. It seemed still and cold and all you could hear was the beeping of taxis, the odd groups of people laughing and calling out. We got to the back of the club and he pushed me to the wall and started to kiss me, his tongue darting in and out, his hands pulling at my pants, he was breathing heavily.

"Do you like this?" he said.

"Yes," I answered.

Although I thought, Not really.

He kissed me harder and every now and then we thankfully stopped for air. His fingers were in my pants. I was getting used to it and it felt OK. I guessed this is what getting off was all about and I couldn't wait to tell the others all about it. I glanced at my watch. Ten past two, I was vaguely worried about getting home but enjoying the moment too much to care.

The door at the back of the club opened and two girls were putting out crates. We froze until they had gone back in and we heard the bolts go back on the door.

We kissed again, harder and more urgent. He slipped his hand back in my pants and pushed a finger inside me.

"Do you like this?" he said.

I wasn't sure I did. "Yes." I said.

He pushed his finger in more and pulled my body down until we were kneeling on the floor, his other hand now inside my bra.

I heard his zip and all at once he took my hands and pressed it to him. I felt his, you know, his dick. I suddenly realised that he was thinking of sex. I flinched away.

"I've got to get back to Katie." I said trying to stand up.

"No you don't, you prick tease, you've been getting me to this state all night, you can't just walk away now." He pulled me to him.

"No, I am not sure, I mean, I've not... not here, it's late, I've . . ."

He face pressed to mine and I couldn't speak any more, I tried to push him back but his weight pushed me down, my back against the hard cold concrete. He shifted himself on top of me and moved my pants to one side. He thrust one, two, three fingers in me. I tried to push him off. He moved his hand and used it to hold me back. I tried to kick out, but his weight on my legs immobilised me.

Then I felt him enter me, thrusting into me. I screamed out in pain.

"You see you bitch, you love it, it's what you wanted, what you needed you fat whore." Out of nowhere came applause. Slow purposeful clapping.

"Give it to her hard, the fat slag, she's loving it," came a voice. The thrusting continued. The more I pushed up, the harder he pushed down, his hand now across my mouth.

"Come on Paul, it's got to be my turn now."

I turned my head to see where the voice was coming from. In the outline of the darkness from the one small light on the back wall, I saw three other guys that I had seen in the bar. One of them already had his dick in his hand. I saw it was hard.

Paul stopped thrusting and pulled out. I felt it warm and wet running between my legs. He held his hand across my face as he moved round and put my head in his lap in a deadlock. I tried to kick out; I felt the heel of my shoe hit the other guy.

"You fucking bitch." He said and he lay on me. I squeezed my legs together.

"Give me a hand guys, the whore is getting frigid."

More laughter. I tried to shout, but Paul's hand was pressed hard against my face. I tried to breathe through my nose, but it was full of snot, I couldn't breathe through my mouth or nose, I panicked.

Both my legs were pulled open, one guy holding each as the other one thrust himself into me. Harder and faster than before, and heavier. My top was round my neck and my skirt around my middle, my arms tucked under Paul's legs and his weight making them numb. I couldn't move. I couldn't speak. Harder and harder it felt until he pulled out and again it was wet and warm.

"Fuck me, I needed that." He said. He put his hands in between my legs, I could feel it wet.

"Taste the fun you fat slag." He said as Paul took his hand momentarily off my mouth. I bit his fingers as he pushed them across my mouth. This prompted him to recoil before tightening his fist and slamming it into my mouth.

The force sent my head into Paul's chest, the pain making me yelp out, I heard a crunch. I could taste blood. My tongue felt a tooth in my mouth, I went to spit but Paul spotted and said "Not on me you dirty slut." He put his hand back over my mouth. "Better quieten down sister." He said.

Another lad then entered me, they were clearly enjoying this. They were encouraging each other, remarking on what an easy lay I was, holding me tight and obviously liking the struggle as the more I kicked the harder they held, punched or kicked.

Then a fourth guy took his turn. He said it was no good, he said I was too wet. Paul twisted my head; the pain was immense so my body followed as he pushed my face down on his trousers into his groin.

Then, as if I didn't know pain already, I knew it then. He entered me from behind I tried to scream out but I could not open my mouth.

All I could do was swallow the blood. I couldn't kick; my legs were the wrong way, my arms twisted behind me. It didn't stop, again and again and again, harder deeper, tearing, unimaginable pain.

Then I wet myself. That provoked the guy who was on me to kick me in the ribs again and again calling me dirty, a whore, and a retard. Paul loosened his grip; I took my chance to scream just before a blow on my head came. Everything blurred, I fell onto my back. I tried to speak, all I felt was blood. As I lay on my back I felt a hand between my legs again and fingers inside me.

I could hear their voices, but I couldn't make out the words. I then felt something hard, solid and cold enter me, then they pulled it out. I knew it was a bottle. Then they pushed it in, this time it felt huge, too big, and I tried to crawl away pushing my body with my legs.

Then came the kick and I heard the crunch as the bottle broke. Everything was blurred, the stars rolling in the sky, the footsteps lessened, the voices, the clapping on the backs, the cold air on my thighs, the warmness of the wetness turning colder. I turned my head to let some blood dribble out. I could smell them, urine and something else that was just vile. My head throbbed. I couldn't move. I was unsure whether the thump, thump thumping was still the bass of the club or my head.

I just closed my eyes.

Now: **That Same Call**

"Sarah, are you OK?" Katie's voice seemed frustrated, urging Sarah to respond.

Sarah opened her eyes, trying to blink away the memory. "Sarah, please talk to me. God this is hard."

"Katie. I am here. You made me remember. What do you mean it was you that called for help? It was an anonymous call I was told, where were you, why didn't you come over to me? I didn't see you . . . all I remember was . . ."

"Sarah, it doesn't do to remember, I am sorry, maybe I shouldn't have called."

"All I remember was blue and white lights . . ."

"Sarah, I am sorry, are you OK?"

"I'm fine. I have to go."

"Can I call you?"

"No!"

"Sarah, after all this time . . ."

"There is nothing to say."

"There is . . ."

"No!"

Sarah put the phone down. A rather rude habit and one Sarah was not proud of, and she had managed it twice in two days now.

Sarah's Story: **White and Blue Lights**

I felt a hand take my wrist.

"I've got her." I heard a woman say.

"Jeeez!" I heard a man say or sort of whistle.

I could smell the pavement. I tried to open my eyes. I couldn't.

I could hear their voices, but I couldn't understand what they were saying. I tried to focus. The voices just kept coming in and out.

"Can you hear me Tamsin?"

Who were they talking to? Who was Tamsin? I didn't respond. Too much effort.

I felt something clamp around my neck and then they rolled me to one side, and then back.

"Tamsin we are taking you to the ambulance." The woman said. I could see blue lights flashing on and off, but I couldn't hear a sound.

They thought I was Tamsin. I opened my mouth to try and speak.

"Don't try and talk, not until later, just rest, we will soon have you comfortable." I lifted my arm to touch my lips, they felt funny. My arm hurt.

I felt a needle go into my hand. I opened my eyes. I was in an ambulance, the white lights hurt, and the lady was staring at me. I tried to look down but the thing around my neck stopped me.

"Does anywhere hurt?" Was she asking me? It hurt below. I couldn't tell her. I just shut my eyes.

"Tamsin, we need to know how much you have had to drink, can you tell us?"

I opened my mouth, I couldn't feel my tooth, I could taste blood, I started to panic, I tried to move my arms, I couldn't, I tried to sit up, pulling.

The man tried to get me to relax. I started trying to lash out. The female moved him away. I stopped trying to move.

She placed her hand on my head and said, "Shhhh, we will soon be there."

The brightness of the hospital was horrible. I was on a bed. Curtains around me opened and closed constantly, everyone was talking. One black skinned man came close to me and said, "We have to take you into the operating theatre, Tamsin, have you had an operation before?"

"I am not Tamsin." Although they must have thought I said, "I am not going."

"You have to go Duckie. We have to get you sorted out."

"Have you had a general anaesthetic Tamsin?"

"Not Tamsin!" It still couldn't come out right.

"You have to my dear. It will feel better soon."

Whatever, I thought, whatever.

The lights went in and out of focus as the trolley seemed to zoom around. I went through big doors into a room of intense light. When I finally got in focus there was a person with a big mask on.

"It's nothing to worry about. We are going to give you something to make you sleepy." They were doing something to my hand "Now count to ten . . ."

I awoke to a dim light and to intense pain in my tummy. Sort of.

A soft voice said, "Welcome back Tamsin, your Mum's waiting to see you."

Reality was flooding back. I wasn't Tamsin and how could they have got my mother? "I'll just get her."

She got up and I watched her go out of the curtains. I heard a voice say, "Let me see her. Is she OK?"

It wasn't my Mother's voice.

"She is doing very well, she has been very brave. She is clearly in some pain, but that will ease soon. There are only so many painkillers we can administer as she has drunk a large quantity of alcohol; we have to be careful. The surgeons are confident they have removed all the glass from her vagina but there is stitching. It looks worse than it is, but it will heal. The surgeon will discuss the care for this area with you. She has lost one front tooth, the other is broken, but the roots are still there. There is lots of swelling to her lips and chin, this will go but she is going to have some heavy bruising. Her arms we know are sore; we are pending an examination of these later. We know there is nothing broken though."

I heard a sob. "Can I see her?"

"Come through. Tamsin lovey, it's your Mum."

I saw this lady appear. I didn't know her. I saw her stare with relief and shock all at once as she gasped, "This isn't Tamsin, Oh thank God." With that she left to nurses gasping apologies at how this mistake had happened. Their voices dimmed rapidly as they walked away.

Holy shit! I thought. I am in serious trouble. I have to get out of here.

As the alcohol worked its way out of my system, I could feel the extent of my injuries. My jaw hurt and I knew I was now due a long overdue trip to the dentist. It hurt below, but not too bad. The nurse had been in and said the police wanted to interview me, but until my parents were here they couldn't. I hadn't expected that. I didn't really want to talk about it.

I slowly climbed out of bed, every bit of me hurting, my arms and legs aching like dead weights. I knelt by the side of my bed and opened the cabinet; there were my clothes in a plastic bag. I pulled them out and stuffed them up the hospital gown. In my purse I had £20.

I left the cubical and made my way down the corridor, bright lights, white and clinical. Identical corridors and lifts, I walked slowly to not raise alarm until I saw a sign for the toilets. The first one felt too near so I went out of the ward and into the main corridor, in the distance seeing more WC signs.

I got in a cubical that smelt of men's urinals and I took off the blue gown and pulled on my clothes. They barely covered me. I felt cold and exposed.

I left the WC and followed the signs for the main entrance. I looked like a hooker. People were staring. I got to reception and hailed a cab home. Agreeing to the fare of £20 he agreed to take me to the door.

There was no one home when I got back. Siblings at school, parents at work.

I ran a bath. I undressed as it ran. The bruises were evident, the cuts evident, my face swollen and bruised.

The clock said 2pm. I sat motionless and stared at the lip shaped clock on the wall and then watched the second hand move round, lulled by the click, click, click, click that it made. All I wanted was a hug.

I wanted someone soft to hold me so I could fall asleep on them. I wanted my Mum. I pulled my knees to my chest, my legs stiff and achy, the pain on my thighs made worse by pulling my legs tightly to me. Wrapping my arms around my legs, I slowly started to rock myself as I cried silently to myself, longing for someone to hold me. Over and over again the events of the last twenty-four hours pounded my head, and without thinking I started to dig my nails into my flesh to feel pain, just to feel something.

I knew that if I told anyone what had happened what the outcome would be. This was my secret now. I did not want to be judged. I did not want to be told what I had done was wrong or make a police statement or anything else. I just wanted to forget about it.

I also still wanted that hug and I wanted to be told it was OK and not my fault. I wanted someone else to take the responsibility and worry. But I couldn't, I just couldn't tell anyone.

Now: **Sarah's Mother Figure?**

Sarah has been exploring the notion that she views Susannah as a Mother Figure. Sarah had even discussed it with her. As if a friendship needed such over analysis. Sarah cannot stop wondering what the attraction was and what she really needed from her.

Sarah asked me continually what was wrong with her and why she was feeling like this. Sarah explained that she was normally so level headed about everything, and the way she was feeling was almost like going back to when she was eighteen.

Some days Sarah seems odd and she wants to be distant from me, from everything. Other days she told me she felt that she wanted Susannah to hold her and tell her everything would be OK.

Sarah confided that she had thought about kissing Susannah a few times over the last year, but that something seemed terribly wrong about her feeling like that, after all, Sarah kept telling me she knew she was not gay. Sarah was in a constant dilemma and admitted that she didn't consciously want to think about Susannah, but she just did. Whatever the job, whatever the problem, she would think of her and seek approval.

I asked Sarah about this. Sarah realized her friendship with Susannah was unhealthy. I agreed with her. Sarah said that it felt more like a relationship. She questioned that that's not how friendship should feel - is it? Sarah told me she had not made friends since she was fifteen. She told me she didn't really care to know people, and that she certainly didn't want them to know her. Sarah told me she was really genuinely happy with that.

I didn't truly believe her...

I wondered if, when she had episodes like this, that she was still that young girl of eighteen, wanting a hug, a hug that never came.

Now: **My Call**

Sarah picked up the phone and dialled Katie's number. Even though she never intended to call, she had written down the number from caller I.D. out of habit more than anything.

Sarah found doodles fascinating. Around Katie's name she had drawn a series of closed-in boxes with bars on them and arrows facing downwards. Sarah used to like reading doodle analysis articles and recalled these are somehow showing inner negative emotion.

That figured then.

"Katie here," Golly. She sounded chirpy.

"It's Sarah her," Sarah waited, unsure of her reaction. She sounded over the moon when she did speak, though goodness knows why.

"Hey, it's great you called. I was thinking of you, look, I am sorry I must have dragged up painful memories."

"You did a little," Sarah answered honestly.

"Look, I need to ask you. I don't understand how you saw what happened but that no one knew. I sort of can't put the bits together. Why didn't you come over when they left me and why didn't you wait by me for help?"

"Sarah, I was by you, I never let you out of my sight. I was scared; I thought they would come back. I was so frightened. It took me ages to find a phone box, I called the police, but they put me through to ambulance, although they came too. I hid all the time they were there. I then got a taxi to Debbie's. I told them you had had an accident. We stayed up until the morning and then Nina's mum came back screaming at us. We were all grounded. We did not want more trouble."

"But you had your own mind Katie."

"True. Now I see that, I saw that years ago. But at the time I didn't see that, it was too big a deal."

"When I went back to school I was so lonely. When I tried to speak out about being raped, do you remember in that English debate? You called me a liar."

"I had to Sarah for your sake, thinking of your future, it was the only way to have got you off subject."

"I was branded a liar after that, no one would come near me, none of you would talk to me."

"I know. I am sorry. You had spoken out in the debate about how you had been raped and that it was your fault for what you were wearing. That was way against the grain of the debate, it sounded weird, and you weren't making sense."

"Katie, I had one hell of a lot of trauma inside me, I wanted people to know I wanted to talk about it."

"I realise that now, at the time all I could see is that you would have got into more trouble . . ."

Then she almost whispered in shame, ". . . I would have got into trouble for not doing something."

"I want to say I understand, but I don't. After that I hated you so much, I used to stick pins in your photos and wish you dead. When I saw you had gone to the same college I hated you even more, you were a memory every day."

"Sarah. I watched you try to die. I saw you take the pills in the common room, I called Jo. You were so thin, so drawn and so, well, ill. You were all over the place; no one could have reached out to you."

She continued, "After that I went to see Jo and I told her what had happened, you know, in your past. It was the first time I had spoken about it. It helped me, and I hoped she would be able to help you.

Then after hospital, I heard you had gone away. I longed to see you, but you never came back. I never knew what was going on with you, and there was no one I could ask. What happened to you then?"

With Sarah's mind now filled with past events, she mumbled something and put the phone down . . . again. Sarah sat on the sofa and stared at the oak tree.

"My oak tree," thought Sarah "So strong, with roots larger than its canopy, a tree that seemingly dies every year and comes to life again every spring with bright new leaves and a new growth. But a tree is only wood. Wood that burns to nothing but ash at the whim of disease or the force of human intervention.

Are we not all living things made of the same matter? Are we like the tree, growing stronger and sturdier every day?

Is our childhood the roots that give you the solid grounding to become strong and grow tall? Without those roots, like the tree, we would surely not grow to our true potential but fall in a storm. What if the roots were rotten?

In human terms what makes our roots? Our life experience? Our past lives? Or is it the people we meet or those we hold onto around us?"

Sarah's mind churned over. Her stability and her very core had been rocked.

Sarah's Story: **Home Recovery**

I am in a darker place now.

Things had changed at home. There was this secret. The more I had to tell lies to cover up things, the more I closed up, the more withdrawn into myself I became.

I carried on as normal, hiding the secret. I re-read every Enid Blyton book from my childhood, reading so I could escape to any place, where I could be someone else and live someone else's life. I listened to music and started to dream about living another life, of being another person.

I never told Mum. I never went to get the dissolvable stitches checked and I never went for a check up. No one knew.

I went back to school. No one would speak to me. I tried to talk to my friends but they walked away. They had each other. I became disruptive in class and utterly rude. I swore at the teachers and was outside of the classroom more than I was in it, which suited me. I was in detention most nights, but that was also OK as there was nothing to do, or go home for, after school. No hugs.

At home, my room became my prison. The self hatred within me raged like a forest fire, eating my very being.

Then one day, I was cutting an apple into slices when the knife slipped and sliced into my thumb. The pain broke through the mental blocks and at last allowed me to feel something. Something other than the emotions otherwise consuming me. I left the apple and went to my room. Laying tissues on the desk, I watched every bright red drop absorb onto them, slowly but surely covering sheet after sheet. When the blood threatened to stop I tore at the cut skin, begging it to bleed more. The pain of pulling the skin gave me a chance to feel a new level of pain that somehow felt so good. It soon became an addiction.

I refused to do PE. I could not bear taking my clothes off. I would be rude, scream and stamp to get sent to the head rather than undress. Getting wise to my behaviour after eight weeks of detentions, Miss Benton took me to her office and told me to change in there. She said she had all day to wait if need be.

After some time, refusing to co-operate and getting fed up of her kindness and patience, I decided I may as well change.

I am not sure if she was shocked to see my body, or alarmed. She asked me who had made all the cuts to my skin. I told her I had. She told me to get dressed, which I did and she called the school nurse. The nurse looked at the cuts and asked me why I was doing it to which I replied I liked to feel the pain. She called my Mum.

Mum was distressed to get the call and she screamed the duration of the way home, and some, but I tuned out before the engine was started. After all, I knew she was ashamed at the trouble I was bringing home. I knew she didn't know what to do with me and I knew she found it hard to love me whilst I was intent on causing others so much pain.

As soon as she left me alone, I took out the art scalpel and started carving into my flesh with ease. The pain somehow easing the pain inside and bringing with it relief. I could then cry as I dipped TCP on the fresh lacerations.

I was worried about being pregnant. The incident was now nearly three months ago. I punched myself repeatedly in the stomach hour upon hour, every day. Then I started to bleed. I was freaked out and called Mum.

"It's just your period love." She said, like I didn't know. "Towels are in the bathroom." I couldn't bear it. I bunked school the next day to go to the library. I had to find a way of stopping the bleeding. I found out the best two ways were repeating the pill with no gaps and becoming anorexic. So I set to work on a plan.

The following day I got an appointment to see the doctor and asked to go on the pill. He said he was not able to refuse and he was happy to prescribe. Mission accomplished.

I then set about how to become anorexic. In theory, it meant simply not eating. In reality, it meant finding a way to skip meals. I couldn't escape eating with the family at breakfast and tea if I was in the house, so I had to find ways I could be out.

Mum said working was a good idea, the paper round in the morning she said would help shift my weight, and the restaurant work in the evening, she said, would probably increase me twofold! She approved anyway.

I could now skip breakfast and tea, and it got me out the house. I could now focus on getting the periods to stop. I was twelve stone in weight with a BMI of thirty; my dress size was an adult eighteen which did put me in the obese category, so losing weight was a good idea.

Sarah's Story: **Countdown**

As the months went by, I became absorbed in a more hectic lifestyle where the loss of my friends didn't matter. I was out at 6am to do two paper rounds before school and I left for work at 5pm explaining that I could eat at work.

I had a diet of one tomato a day. I had to focus every bit of energy on not eating to become anorexic. The weight was falling off too. I had dropped several sizes in two months, but no one was really noticing anything. I wore the same clothes.

I worked as much as I could at the restaurant. Five nights a week and double shifts over the weekend. I was a good silver service waitress and management liked the way I did not get involved with other staff. I came in, worked and left and this got me promoted to head waitress. I would get in at midnight most nights and cut myself. I knew I was not losing weight quick enough so the answer was to cut it out, bit by bit.

I recall one night not having the courage to dig deeper and getting the bottle of whisky from the alcohol cabinet and swigging from the bottle through the early hours as I cut into my flesh. The feeling of pain was euphoric and the alcohol dimmed my reactions. It became a nightly habit. As the weight dropped, my grades at school went up. I was swotting for GCSEs and yet working every hour I could, cutting myself into the early hours. The stamina I found was unreal and unlike anything I have known since.

The downside was the darker feelings. I was so alone. I didn't really talk to anyone; in fact I avoided situations where I may have to speak. I would hide around corners or in toilets just to not have to look at someone and say hello. I felt worthless. I felt alone and I felt like there wasn't really much point in living. I would sit for hours on my own, thinking about death and how I could die.

I did decide to see how the exams panned out though. The plans I had for my funeral had me remembered as a grade 'A' student. It would be a waste to do anything before this was established. These ironic moments were what kept me sane.

I passed everything, not all grade A but mostly A or B a few C's but 12 GCSEs which wasn't bad. Mum said well done but was more proactive in telling everyone in the village how proud she was, rather than tell me directly. I was due to go to college after the break, so spent the holidays earning money and working three jobs as I added pub work to the restaurant and paper rounds.

By the time I started college, I had lost another four stone and it was very noticeable. At eight stone, I was now a bit bigger than normal, but not much. I used my money to buy new clothes that hid my body as much as I could and chose to layer myself up to hide both my weight and the marks. I was still set on dying, but I decided that I would become so small first so no one would know I had finally gone. I didn't want the drama of anything more than that. There was no concern over the weight loss, as sudden as it was.

People were actually congratulating me on how well the diet was going. I rode along with that. My diet still consisted of tomatoes, Calypso ice lollies and McCoy's chilli crisps.

Sarah's Story: Jo

Keeping the three jobs proved hard with college so, after the Christmas break, I quit the paper round. Anorexia now had me in its control.

People were noticing. I was passing out on the train and at college and at work. Mum had started to worry and this lead to vicious rows. My weight was now hovering around the seven stone mark.

Theatrical production kept me alive. I loved performing and being someone else. I absorbed myself Stanislavski-style into every character. I was in the college drama group and the course involved bi-termly productions. I had a central role in the Sound of Music and was in every production, singing and dancing to the best of my ability. Unlike my peers who were out drinking and clubbing, I would rehearse until I was polished.

During the last week of rehearsals for the Rocky Horror Show, I fainted coming down the stairs. I slipped on the microphone lead I think, but I tumbled a fair way. It was the bit where I, as Magenta, was leaping from the balustrades in the time warp. I will maintain I lost my balance, everyone said I passed out mid-song line. It was possibly a bit of both. I had hit my head pretty hard. I came round in Jo's office to find her stroking my head and holding a cold compress. I warmed up instantly. Greta, my tutor was by her. They both looked worried. They saw my eyes were open.

"Sarah, glad your back with us. When did you last eat?"

I hadn't a clue. It was Wednesday, I think I last ate on Saturday, but I wasn't sure. I looked down and saw my basque had slipped around so the long bits were not covering one of the cuts. I quickly adjusted it, probably too late and too obviously.

"This morning," I lied.

Greta laughed, "Oh, that will be the large bowl of air then Sarah"

I smiled. No pulling wool over her eyes.

"Sarah." Greta always made a point of touching my arm as she spoke. It was kind of reassuring. "Sarah. When I carried you . . ."

Oh God, they know I weigh a ton now, how awful. Carried me?

"I noticed the cuts to your side. Are you self harming?"

Shit!

"Sarah, how much do you weigh?"

Double shit!!

I sat up. "I am fine, honest. I just skipped brekkie, I will be fine after lunch."

The sudden lack of blood draining from my brain made me woozy and dizzy. I could hardly focus. Jo put her arm on mine to steady me.

"Another bowl of air, this time with thin air for dessert," smiled Jo. "Come on Sarah. Let me give you a ride home."

"No." I said. "It's OK, really."

"I would like a chat with your Mum."

"I am over 16. You can't."

"And underweight, starving and self harming."

"And I will kill myself if you take me home."

Why I said it I don't know. Somewhat ironically, it stopped them dead. "I don't want to go home." I said.

"Sarah, would you like to stay for a few days with me," said Jo, "but only if your parents agree."

I nodded.

"So can I take you home so you can get your things? I will tell your Mum you have a heavy schedule."

I nodded, "Thanks."

"One condition?" Jo added, "You will have something to eat."

Triple shit!!!

Jo drove me home. It took forever; you forget distance travelling by train. We didn't speak the whole journey, but it didn't feel awkward. I just shut my eyes, happy that someone else was taking responsibility.

During the long silence, I could tell she seemed nervous. I was angry.

As we pulled in the drive Jo blurted, "Does your Mother realise you are anorexic?" I shrugged.

"When did your Mother last see you without your clothes on?"

I laughed thinking what a strange question. "I dunno, couple of years back?" I actually knew the exact time. "Jo, you aren't going to say anything, are you? We had a deal."

"Let's go in."

"Not until you promise me."

"That's not going to happen."

"Then you lied, you cow."

"Sarah. I have never lied to you."

"Just leave me here."

"No!"

This conversation was going too quickly for me. I got out and slammed the car door shut, let myself in and then slammed the front door. I went upstairs to pack.

When I came down I heard Mum and Jo talking. I went into the kitchen. Mum looked livid. She hated people being involved in the family.

"Jo said you're going to stay with her for a few weeks until after the performances."

"Is that OK?" I asked, not really caring what the answer was.

"Of course darling, if that's what you want." She spoke through gritted teeth, sounding false and insincere.

"Come on then," I said to Jo. Jo didn't move.

"Mrs...... Lamb, excuse me for bringing this up but . . ."

"Jo!"

"Do you think Sarah is anorexic?" She continued, "It just I have some experience and I think-"

Mum turned sharply and sighed, "Sarah is just doing what most teens do, losing the puppy fat and shaping up. She needed to lose weight and-"

"Don't you think she may have lost enough and is now taking it too far though, Mrs. Lamb?"

"Hello? I am here you know," I protested.

"Mrs. Lamb, has Sarah seen a Doctor?"

"Jo, it is Jo isn't it?" Jo nodded.

"Sarah is perfectly fine, a normal rebellious teenager with mood swings to boot. She doesn't need a doctor. She just needs to grow out of it."

I was quite impressed. See, nothing wrong with me, let's get on with it. I kissed Mum on the cheek and said my goodbyes and we went to Jo's car. Jo was pretty hacked off by the exchange, but then I just thought I did warn her not to interfere.

We drove in silence and then Jo said, "This killing yourself remark, what was all that about?"

"Nothing!"

"It's not normal to come out with that sort of thing though Sarah."

"I was just messing."

"Are you OK? Is everything OK?"

"Yup!"

"You can talk to me," she said.

"All is fine Jo. I just need a break," I said thinking what I really wanted was a break from life.

I had told the restaurant I was away for two weeks. They changed the rota with minor grumbling.

Sarah's Story: **Anchoring My Arse**

Jo's home was so arty it was almost confusing. It was not tidy, it was not all that clean and not at all like home. There seemed to be a cat on every available sofa or chair and she had a crazy parrot mumbling away in the corner eyeing me up and down.

"Arse to anchor," he said and I laughed.

"Don't mind Henry Sarah, he gets that phrase from my father who had Henry before he passed over."

"Passed over what?"

"Died. Gone to the other place."

"Oh!"

"Make yourself at home, what can I get you?"

"Just water is fine thanks Jo."

"Sarah, let's get one thing clear, you are not dying on my watch, so what would you like to eat?"

"I don't do eating."

"You will do here."

"Jo, please, don't make me. I can't"

"Yes Sarah, you can, but no worries for now. Ruth and Jo junior as we call her will be in soon so they will no doubt be starving, if we wait for Sammy to get back we can eat together."

"I thought you had two daughters," I said.

"I do. Jo is Ruth's partner."

"Oh!"

"You get used to it." Jo said.

Jo was right. Madness descended when Ruth came home, falling over the cat with her various bags flying everywhere. She burst in giving Jo a huge hug and over the noise of Henry flapping, the cat hissing she said, "Love you, Mother dearest" and giving her a huge kiss to match.

Jo junior also grabbed Jo and said her hellos and flopped down in a huge armchair narrowly missing a cat that was so fat it could be mistaken as a cushion.

"Ruthie, this is Sarah, she staying for a week or so."

Ruthie came over and grabbing me plonked a kiss on each cheek.

"Welcome to the mad house Sarah, what did you do to land a week with my mother in the madhouse, commit murder? Or just not learn your lines?"

"Sarah's memory is pretty amazing for learning scripts Ruthie, I've told you this before."

Ruth grinned, "So that's how you bag the best parts is it? Magenta!"

"Sarah can act too, Ruthie, but line learning is something of a particular help, and Sarah also can sing which is good - Sarah sing 'Touch me' to Ruth it's her favourite!"

I wanted to die there and then, this was too much attention, too crazy, I was not singing 'Touch me' to an 'out and proud' lesbian either. Playing a part was one thing, reality another. I needed quiet.

"No, I don't think I could Jo."

Ruth gave me a gentle rub on the back and whispered, "Chill chick, don't look so scared." I smiled gratefully.

"Sarah, this is Jo junior. We call her that because Old Jo gets confused." I felt myself laughing again.

"Jo has been in the studio all day recording tracks, would you like to hear?" I nodded. "Let's get the track on Jo." Jo rummaged in her bag obligingly. Old Jo came in. "Before you ladies go into the world of song and dance, can we talk supper?"

"Starving," said Jo and Ruth together

"Any requests?"

"Pizza and Chianti." Ruthie said and Jo groaned,

"Pasta for me Jo, please."

In the chaos, I heard the front door open and in flew a stunning willowy blond, stick thin and almost floating.

"Hey gang," she yelled as she too came into the room and flopped in between Jo and Ruth. "Did I hear Pasta? Perfect."

Jo turned to me. "Pizza or pasta Sarah?" I shook my head

"Jo, nothing really, I can't."

"OK Sarah, but trust me, everything is soluble in a bottle of wine."

Jo left to cook and Sammy, Jo and Ruth chatted non stop, teasing, laughing, throwing cushions, and then as supper came through they cleared the huge coffee table to make room. Jo bought in bowls of pasta with sauce, garlic bread, two huge pizzas and two bottles of red wine. A feast that smelled amazing.

As Ruth filled everyone's glass with wine, Jo went out and came back in with a large bowl of iceberg lettuce and sliced tomatoes.

"Dig in." She said, subtly placing the iceberg in front of me.

It felt uncomfortable not to eat anything, and it smelled so good. I helped myself to a little iceberg and nibbled on it, sipping red wine that instantly made me feel better and more relaxed.

Ruth leaned back after inhaling her bowl of pasta, and mopping up the sauce with garlic bread, she announced that she was stuffed and undid her button. I estimated a size twelve. Jo was a little larger, a fourteen and Sam a six or eight. I was ten.

"Sarah," she said, "you are so tiny, but no wonder. You don't eat much, do you?"

I smiled. "Enough, it's just been a long day."

"How can you be so strong to not eat this garlic bread?" She said helping herself to more.

"I can't," I said and helped myself to one. The red wine was clearly dissolving my will power.

The evening seemed to go on forever and I felt so comfortable. When I lay in bed, I could still hear everyone chatting downstairs, it just felt so right.

Sarah's Story: **Acceptance**

The following evening, I was determined not to eat.

I was one night away from performance and even Twiggy would struggle in fishnets and a basque. Ruth was on her own and bored so suggested I try on some of her tops for the after show parties at the end of the week. I didn't want to but I agreed.

Ruth wouldn't let me take the clothes and go to my room; she couldn't really understand the concept of privacy. She walked around in her bra most of the time.

As I took my top off she gasped, "What the fuck Sarah?"

She grabbed me. "What the fuck are you doing to yourself, Jesus Sarah, this is awful? Does my Mum know?"

I nodded trying to cover up my stomach. She stared in disbelief. "I don't get it? You are gorgeous, why would you do this to yourself?"

I would rather not have a lesbian call me gorgeous and pulled at my top to get it back on, embarrassed.

"Sorry," was all I could mutter.

"Why?"

"I don't really want to talk about it if that's OK."

"But Sarah lovely," she sat on the bed and pulled me to sit beside her and she gave me a hug. At last.

"Mum said you were anorexic, though that's obvious, she never told me about this, I mean, why should she? But you know, this is crazy, Sarah."

I leant into her. She smelt of pears soap. My head was on her chest. She stroked my hair. I felt comforted. She stroked my cheek and wiped away a tear that had fallen.

"Sarah?" I looked at her. We were so close. Our eyes locked together. I then got this strange notion that she may try to kiss me, I broke away and grabbed the rest of my clothes and practically ran out of the room, slamming the door as I left.

It spoilt the atmosphere in the house a little with her and Jo clearly discussing me. I couldn't look at Ruth, who seemed to always be looking at me.

The following day we did two run-throughs of the play and I was shattered. So shattered I fell asleep in the dressing room at the mirror. Jo came in and told me the cast were worried I was going to pass out, thus wrecking the show. They were calling for Sadie, my wisely appointed understudy, to step in. I got up and walked into the social room and sat next to Bex who was playing Janet.

"Bex, I hear everyone is freaking about me fainting in performance."

"Yup, you gotta eat Sarah."

"OK, what do you suggest?"

"Really? OK, let's get soup and a roll from the canteen."

I reluctantly went and ate. I forced down every mouthful to the delight of Bex, and when we got back she spread the word and everyone seemed to relax a little and the tension in the atmosphere lifted. Greta came and told me Jo was pleased too.

The performance was fine. I gave it everything, held the high notes and even got the laughs in Touch Me. The theatre was packed with everyone joining in and I heard people were buying up repeat performance tickets for the week.

That evening I was exhausted and as I stood on the scales realised they had finally fallen under six stone and felt a surge of happiness.

The week's performances were truly the best adrenaline rush anyone could want. The physical and emotional energy saw the scales hit five and a half stone and the clothes were hanging off me.

I moved back home and nested back into my own bed. I quit the restaurant as I realised the energy was too much and that I would need to eat. Whilst I wasn't eating I was dropping weight, and that was preferable. Despite feeling happy about the weight loss, the drastic food reduction was making me have constant thoughts about death and dying.

I started to sleep more and more, and as I drank less and less was having horrendous headaches and dizziness. I thought of everything in minuscule detail, and let my imagination take me to new places.

I started creating a fantasy world on the edge of the real world; I started to confuse what was real and what was my imagination. I woke up unsure of whether things had happened or not. In my vivid daydreaming, people took on new forms; people were talking about me, plotting. In others, I was in the arms of Ruth clinging to the softness and smell of pears, in others I was floating to new lands and living another life. In one life I was a child living by the sea, in another daydream I was a man living in the mountains tending goats, in another I was dead and floating over the world. I could see me in the body of a young prostitute and recalling feeling alone in my cot when I was young. All these things were reality but were not. In my waking hours of conscious mind, I could not separate fact from fantasy. I was delusional most of the time. I had made up my mind that the other worlds were better, and it was time to leave this one.

I went to college as normal, but didn't make most classes and was found sleeping in the common room. This one afternoon Jo came to find me in the break.

"You have got to get a grip Sarah, look at the state you are in. I do not know what more I can plausibly do to help you. There is nothing more I can say, you won't let me in and you won't let me help. I don't know what is going on, but you are seriously sick and you need help."

As she got closer looking in my eyes she asked, "Have you been drinking?"

"It will be over soon," I said.

"What's that meant to mean?"

As she asked the question, her face grew worried. Looking at my closed fist she grabbed my hand and opened it to reveal an empty packet of aspirin.

Jo grabbed my bag; out fell some packets of sleeping tablets, more aspirin and a bottle of vodka that was two thirds full still.

"Oh well done Sarah, this is really bloody clever and intelligent; now get up because you are going with me right now to the hospital." I didn't move.

"Sarah, if you make me I will scream for help, so get up now." I did.

I followed her to the car. She almost threw me in. As she drove me to A & E, she was just going on about what a waste of a good life, what a waste of talent and how she blamed herself for not doing something. I closed my eyes; she shook me, screaming, "You are not going to bloody sleep!"

Jo pulled up outside A&E; someone must have called ahead as there were nurses waiting at the door. I was put on a trolley and rushed through; Jo was showing them the empty bottle and packets.

"How many of these have you taken?"

"All."

"And these?"

"All."

"When?"

"Are you her Mother?" Someone asked Jo.

"No."

"We have to pump her stomach fast. She must drink this."

I can't tell you the next part of this because I don't recall it very well. I recall drinking something that I spat out, and then I recall them forcing tubes down my throat and pulling them out as I was sick, time and time and time again, a ripping burning sensation at the back of my throat that was to ultimately damage my vocal chords.

My mind was in a warm cosy place, I was happy, bathed in light and a feeling of tranquillity, free from physical aches and calm. Such calmness. I could hear voices whispering to me, but I couldn't hear what they were saying over the noise from the room below me. Doctors were shouting at me and pulling me from this place.

I kept trying to close my eyes to return to the light, but was being pulled back to the ward; I fought them off as hard as I could. I had drips forced into me and no end of people fussing over me. It was evening before I remembered much. Jo had been and gone and most of the time it was just me alone. But no matter how hard I tried to go back to my dreamland, I couldn't. The warm cozy place had gone. It seemed out of reach.

I was told that I was to be admitted to hospital for a while, and if I attempted to discharge myself they would section me under the Mental Health Act.

I accepted this and did not argue.

Now: **Another Call**

The normal rush at the end of the day had begun and Sarah had just collected her child and had started to prepare the evening meal. Sarah was looking forward to a glass of wine to unwind from the day.

Sarah instinctively knew the phone was about to ring, so turned down the gas in anticipation. It was not until the phone did ring a few seconds later that Sarah thought how bizarre it was.

"Hello?"

"Sarah, it's Katie, do you have a moment?"

"Sure."

"You sounded a little upset last time we spoke, and I don't want that. I didn't call to rake over the past, I called to try and make up the past and move forward."

"Katie, I moved forward a long time ago. For me this really is history, and to be honest, since you called I have not maintained any focus. It's really thrown me, I didn't really want this all bought up again"

Sarah didn't want to be harsh, but the truth was Sarah was finding it really difficult. She was not going to tell Katie any of this; she was still struggling to understand why Katie had called her after all this time.

Sarah was feeling like she was stuck in a loop and being forced to go back in time with constant flashbacks and constant emotions surfacing.

For a long time Sarah had always locked emotions away, keeping herself to herself and dealing with things.

Sarah confided in me that it felt like so much that had been bottled up was now wanting to come out, like a pressure valve at maximum but she couldn't understand why it should be this way. She was doing fine; there was no reason for her to feel like this.

Sarah knew it was affecting her emotionally. The irregular and sometimes dormant bulimia had come back with a rage and she confided in me that she was eating and puking three times a day, anything to try and find some sort of release.

Sarah at this point confided that the depression she was falling into was scaring her. Every other week since the call she had experienced days where she felt bone crushingly low, unable to move from the dark cloud that overshadowed her.

A little while ago: **Susannah**

Sarah has always believed that we meet people for a reason, a season or a lifetime. She also believes that there is no such thing as a chance meeting. Sarah will tell anyone that whilst we may not know it at the time, we may never understand it or value it, there is a reason... and a rhyme.

Sarah explained that, after the call from Katie, and after the events came flooding back, that she clung to Susannah. She told Susannah out of the blue that she was a pretty vulnerable person. Susannah had given Sarah a hug. Sarah has told me that she could have stayed in that embrace for a long time, just feeling the compassion and warmth of a woman.

Sarah didn't realise that because the raw emotions of her past that were running through her were so uncomprehendingly strong she could be experiencing something different.

All Sarah knew was that she could stay feeling comforted by Susannah for a long time. However, from all Sarah was sharing, there seemed to be patterns in her behaviours emerging, and that in these similar episodes Sarah always said she felt like something else was taking over, and that she wasn't herself.

On this occasion I was grateful Sarah felt she could feel connected to someone so understanding.

Sarah explained to me this is why she can so Appreciate Angels, because when she looks back, she can see people who have picked her up and helped her. There but by the grace of God.

Someone told Sarah, out of the blue today, that there are angels walking the earth alongside us. Sarah didn't say Susannah is an angel but she noticed that she was there at exactly the point in time she needed someone to be supportive of her.

Sarah believes that Angels are surrounding us and influencing our life and almost certainly those 'chance' meetings.

Sarah's Story: **Sunshine Sarah**

My time in hospital, in itself, was not real.

It was where a performer polished her act, a place where I had no feelings and my heart turned to stone. I recall little of the detail because I purposely shut my mind and just did all I could to get out. I started to build a wall around me.

I learnt three things in hospital. How to lie, how to cheat and how to manipulate. As a result, I got out quickly.

I also learnt not to trust psychologists as they don't tell, or know, the truth.

They are all looking to over analyse you as a subject of their own next medical research paper just to further their own careers. I am not convinced about them caring about the welfare of the patient. I certainly was presented as a specimen. I felt as thought I was a creature in a jar, being observed by lots of nodding-dog students. I never knew what was in the long winded notes they wrote as they were never discussed with me.

Sitting in the therapist's chair I was asked, "Why do you want to die Sarah?"

To which I would reply, "Why do you want to know, doctor?"

"Why do you feel the need to be defensive Sarah?"

"Why do you feel the need to patronise me doctor?"

It went on like this for a week. The nurses were no better. "Now Sarah, you must eat your dinner"

"And why may that be nurse?"

"You know if you don't eat we have the right to force feed you via a tube."

"And do you see that as right and fair nurse? Do you see that as helping?"

"Sarah, yes we do because you are not well enough to make up your own mind." So I gave up fighting. I became compliant. I ate.

I answered questions to why do you want to die with, "Oh I don't, I love life, it was a moment of stupidity, attention seeking."

And so it went on. So did the pounds.

I was able to go home after four weeks as I was demonstrating, "A sincere attempt to get well and a positive and responsible mental attitude to my own well being."

What crap! They didn't get inside my head; they just taught me to play the game. Stupid.

One of the other patients told me that to get out off the ward all I had to do was agree, be positive and to play out a part and under no circumstances lose my temper, and that as soon as I got out I could concentrate on my dieting again. The same person introduced me to laxatives as a way of getting rid of food and the notion of puking. People who got out would then smuggle them into the friends and the only condition of accepting was you promised to do the 'lax-run' once you got out.

Once out I went back home to my parents. I sat at the table and picked at the food, the minimum I could before being threatened to being taken me back to hospital. I then swallowed eight - ten laxatives at a time to get rid of it. Whilst I was not bulimic at this point I was not allowed in the first four weeks at home to be left unattended for an hour after eating. It drove me mad. The laxatives gave me crippling stomach pains and made my heart beat go funny and I had the shakes and sweats for hours. Every sip of water would, for the next twelve hours bring on new cramping and sweats. It was not pretty but it seemed the only way to keep the scales balanced in my mind.

I couldn't control what had happened to me, but I could control this. It was utter empowerment. Take away me controlling food, and I knew I had no control on my life.

The problem, with eating, was that I got hungry. My stomach getting used to being fed would start growling if I missed food.

I wanted food, and if I gave in then I would give way in a big way, not just one cream cake, but eight or ten and then I would run to the nearest toilet and stick my fingers down my throat and get rid of it all.

The satisfaction of eating, the positive way it made me feel, the fullness I felt was utterly amazing, fulfilling and just total satisfaction.

But towards the end, as I was so full, with my stomach aches came the complex and unbearable guilt, the self disgust at letting go of my control, and the self hatred which was unbearable. So I had to be sick and I was sick until my throat was red raw, until tears streamed down my face, until I physically couldn't purge anymore. The effort left my knees weak and me feeling exhausted. This started a cycle that was going to stay for a long time.

As humiliating it was, as disgusting it sounds, it felt good and kept me in control of something.

I longed to get back the control of anorexia though. There was no way however that I could do this at home. So I made the decision to leave.

Whilst at home I noticed my mother reading a magazine called The Lady. Out of boredom, I decided to read it and I noticed an advert for a live-in waitress and hostess for a country hotel in a small village in Somerset. It catered for various festivals and was a well reputed place for business people staying over. I applied and to my surprise got the job on a phone interview and the references from the local restaurant.

Not only that I could transfer year two of my 'A' levels to the local college. I didn't hesitate. I informed my mother immediately that I was going and she didn't raise any objection. I packed a suitcase of clothes and headed by train to Somerset. In all honesty, I think everyone was pleased to see the problem child on her way and from under their skin. I had always brought problems to the door and it was not fair on my very private family.

The day I left, no one came to wave goodbye to the train. I said my goodbyes at the doorstep and Mum said, "Sarah, next time I see you, can you try to return to the little 'sunshine Sarah' you once were?"

Even I didn't quite know where she was anymore; maybe I would find her one day? Even I didn't like who I was becoming, at times the old me was still there, but there was something else raging within me.

In time, maybe I would be normal again. It would be good to get to know Sarah again.

Sarah's Story: **The Hotel**

I was greeted off the train by Terry, the hotel porter who was looking out for me having seen my picture that I had sent to the hotel. Terry looked about 80 but moved with the sharpness of someone a lot younger. A little bit crooked, a little unshaven, but with friendly welcoming eyes behind his apparent gruffness.

"Hey you must be Sarah." he said as he picked up my case and bag.

I nodded. "Car's over here." he said leading me out of the small station to the car park. "Hop in."

He opened the door for me, "I bet you are famished travelling all this way on train, soon have you to the Inn, I'm sure you need a good cup of tea and some tucker."

In truth I was hungry. However, now I had left home I was determined not to eat again. One thing I learnt in hospital to avoid food was to declare that I was a vegan, this flummoxed people so you could get away with salad or veg. This was my new mission.

We didn't speak throughout the journey. I just took in the countryside. I was feeling sleepy. The train journey had been long but I didn't dare sleep as I felt strangely vulnerable. The change at London scared me. So many people and everyone seemed to be rushing to be somewhere else. It struck me that if I was going to try to die again, London was the place to do it in, because no one would notice you had disappeared. Amongst all the beggars and the people sleeping rough, nobody would notice one more down and out.

We drove down a lane that seemed to go on forever until we came to a tiny village that was dominated by an imposing castle that was stunning. Imposing, but stunning.

"Them's all tied houses in the village, tied to the Lord."

"I don't understand?" I had not heard anyone say 'Them's' before, and the grammar made me shudder and I did not know what a 'tied house' meant either.

"Means you can only live in this village if you work for the Lord."

I laughed. "Bit like the monks then!"

"Chance of them all behaving like monks would be something," he guffawed back. "Here we are, and see there? Jane and Mark are waiting for you."

As we pulled to a halt, Mark opened the door for me and, as I got out, Jane greeted me with a hug and a kiss on both cheeks. I got it all wrong and didn't turn my head at the right time, so ended up laughing a little embarrassed. I had only seen people do this 'huggy kiss, kiss' thing in the theatre, and it seemed all very grown up.

"Sarah darling, great you made it, welcome to The Inn and this is Mark."

Mark too gave me a hug and kissed my cheeks. I still got it wrong and I felt his lips just touch mine as I did not turn my head in time. We laughed again.

Mark picked up my bags and, leading the way, strode through the oak doors and I followed. We went firstly into reception with its dark wood panelling and then through this area to a huge beamed lounge complete with log fire and countless comfy chairs and sofas all scattered with bright coloured cushions. It looked so homely and relaxing. With my tiredness from the journey now really kicking in, I could just curl up in an armchair and dose.

"This is the lounge Sarah; guests relax in here when they are not in the cellar bar or dining room."

We sailed through this area to the dining room which was a sea of crisp white and yellow linen and masses of silverware. Each table had long stemmed yellow and white roses which gave the room a luxurious feel to it. We went through the staff doors and into the kitchen which was a huge mass of brushed silver units and several chefs were in the throes of pre service prep. It was hot and busy. The three men working there nodded at Mark as we walked through, but carried on with their jobs.

"We are just about to eat Sarah, no doubt you will be hungry after the long journey. This will give you a chance to meet the live-in team."

Leading off the kitchen was the staff common room. Unlike most hotels whose common rooms were tacky, dirty and littered with fag buts and chips, this room had a giant wooden table with bench seats around to easily fit ten or so people. There were flowers on the table, the table was laid properly and the atmosphere was clean and fresh. There were several people at the table already chatting and relaxing.

"Hey folks, this is Sarah who is joining us in the silver service restaurant. Sarah is going to be studying at the college whilst working here. She'll be living in number five. Sarah will also work the cellar bar at weekends and do outside catering for the summer festivals at the Castle."

The others nodded in approval and gave welcoming smiles and budged up the bench to make room for me.

Jane carried on with the introductions. "So, Sarah, this is Angela. Angela's just moved to house eight with Corrine and Sophie."

The girls gave friendly 'hello faces' and 'mini-waves' as they started to tuck into the bowls of salad, chips and pie that had just been brought in by one of the kitchen staff.

I sat down with everyone as Jane started to talk to Corrine about her new room and Mark engrossed himself in football talk with two of the lads, their names I couldn't recall. I poured myself some water.

"Not eating Sarah?" said Jane.

"I'll have some salad thanks, in a moment." I must appear normal I thought

"It's chef's best steak pie Sarah, you don't want to miss it"

"I'm actually a vegan, Jane." Get it in quickly, I thought.

After a brief silence at my announcement, I was then bombarded with questions. "So what do Vegans eat? That's no meat or dairy, is that right? Do you eat eggs?"

"What about things with eggs in? Will you eat that?"

"Gawd, no butter, no cakes? No way!"

"No wonder you are soooo skinny!"

I looked round the table and smiled. This was easy.

"My diet's really balanced and I guess it's a lifestyle choice, I've been vegan for so many years."

"That's why you're so darn skinny, lucky cow." said Angela.

I smiled, "Just lucky genes, I guess?"

When the subject dropped I felt quite pleased with myself. No more questions about what I was, or was not eating, no more fuss over being skinny. I felt really proud. Now I could concentrate on not eating again.

After supper I was shown to my room, it was tiny. It had a single bed, a wardrobe and en-suite loo and shower but there was hardly any floor space. Small but all mine and I loved it.

"If you want to come to the bar, drinks are on us for the first night," said Mark. "However I can see you look tired so no doubt you will want to sleep. In the morning, we will meet in the restaurant at 10, I will go through the job, your rota and your duties and we can go from there. I've no doubt you will settle down quickly and make some great friends."

He left. As soon as my head hit the pillow, I slept. I did not even get undressed or washed.

Sarah's Story: **St Trinian's**

The following morning Mark took me through the rota and the duties in the job.

Mark pointed out the bus routes to get to college. I had to enrol the following week. I already had a sense it was going to be tough - my rota was 7pm to 1am Monday to Friday, making thirty five hours and then 9am to 11pm Saturdays. So a forty-nine hour week at best.

Sundays were my day off, though I could work a shift for additional money giving me £20 for a four hour shift, and I could opt for one or all three shifts if I wanted. My salary for live-in was £200 per week with food provided on top. So all I had to spend was bus fare and book money. I felt decidedly wealthy.

I fitted in really well, I saw everyone pretty much only when I was on shift so it was talk of work and little else. I signed in at college and to my delight had quite a lot of free time and so long as I stayed away from the inn all day I could do my home study and assignments in the library. No need to mix my lives at all. Everyone already knew each other on the course and so I didn't automatically blend it, which suited me as I was there to get my exams and nothing more. I turned down all offers of anything social and eventually people stopped asking.

My social life generally speaking took place in the early hours of the morning after shift. Being blessed with stamina for only needing six hours sleep to function, I found I was coping with the working hours and college. Just.

Having not eaten all day, by the end of shift I was very hungry and loved nothing more than a packed of McCoy's chilli crisps and a pint of Guinness, after which I could relax and join in as my stomach abated for a while. I often joined the live-in staff for meals at a weekend, eating just a little steamed veg or salad. My weight remained a constant six stone, six pounds and I was quite happy with that. I knew if I cut back more I would not have the stamina to get through my hectic lifestyle, but I felt in control.

After just three months, I was fully integrated and it felt like I had been doing it forever. I had stopped cutting myself, no longer took laxatives and rarely was sick. Life it seemed was getting back on track.

Jane was never around in the week; she worked away and came back at weekends. The hotel was much stricter with her presence and late nights were curbed at 2.30am, where as in the week we had been known to still be drinking at 4am.

It was on one Saturday though, in which Jane called to say she was visiting her family. Mark announced that we would have schoolgirls' and headmasters' dressing up party. All staff were invited to the party.

It was the wildest night of my life to that point. After joining in the tequila slamming I knew I was drunk. The room was a little fuzzy and I felt a bit woozy. I decided that I ought to eat something so headed for the kitchen to take some bread. I felt really happy and felt I was making friends.

I dressed in a tiny black skirt of Angela's that many would take for just a belt. I had also borrowed suspenders and fishnets; I wore my restaurant blouse but unbuttoned it halfway down with one of Mark's ties loose round my neck. I think the expression 'schoolgirl slut' would sum up my appearance.

As I took the bread from the bread store, I heard someone behind me and I froze. "Sarah, that you?" I felt relief that it was Mark; the chefs would have gone crazy.

"Sure is Mark, I am feeling a tad pissed, I needed some bread."

"No worries, I wanted to make sure you were alright."

"I'm good thanks."

He leant towards me, I could smell his aftershave. Musty, but sexy.

"Oh I know your good Sarah, Indeed you are very good, and very, very gorgeous and I can't take my eyes off you."

"Mark, get on with you, you soppy mule." I pushed him gently way.

"Come on Sarah, you must want a bit of Marko." He gyrated. "Every girl needs a bit of Marko!"

"Not really, I . . ."

"You're a virgin?" He said, giggling. "Not really, sort of. . ."

"Come on Sarah, I will be real gentle, you know you want a little bit of me." He leaned towards me.

"Sarah sweetheart, you know that you can't resist a man like me."

We started to kiss, it was good and I wanted more. My head giddy with the attention and alcohol, it felt right.

He flicked the kitchen light off. Darkness other than the hum of the refrigerators and neon blue light of the fly zapper. He pushed me against the wall and he was touching me all over and, before I knew it, he had pushed my pants to one side and he was inside me, against that wall, thrusting in and out. In the open kitchen, we were having sex.

It felt so powerful the effect I clearly had on him but I just tuned out, it didn't bother me that we were having sex. I actually couldn't really feel anything. I mean, I knew he was inside me, I knew what we were doing, but I didn't feel anything else. Nothing.

My mind removed totally from my body, like I was watching someone else in the kitchen.

I just thought about whether I would dip some Marmite on the bread or not.

Mark finished and said we ought to get back to the party, I went first and he followed. I never got the bread. I stopped via the loo to make myself look decent again. I wiped his mess away and got all the clothes back on in the right place.

Angela was in the loo reapplying her lip gloss, "Alright Sarah?"

I nodded, "I am feeling a bit wobbly actually. Too much tequila I think!" I went to the loo, and when I came out she had gone back to the bar.

I looked at myself in the mirror. I had just had sex with the boss. I felt really cool and in control. It hadn't hurt like before, in fact it was nothing, it meant nothing and I felt nothing. It was fine. I couldn't get pregnant as I now had a contraceptive hormonal coil that would stop all bleeding and all chance of being pregnant. They understood my fear of bleeding and said this would help.

The rest of the night Mark kept looking at me. I felt so powerful to have him, the big boss, in my power. I teased him all night. As the party grew to a close, I helped clear up. Mark stayed around too. He then said it would be good to finish what we started.

I spend the night in his bed, with Jane's clothes hung around me. I did not sleep. I had this forty five year old man in my grip and I knew I was in control. I loved the feeling of being held so close and so tightly, I felt so secure with my head in his chest and it felt so lovely holding onto someone bigger and stronger. He lay me down and we had sex, we rested, he then put me on top and I felt so much power that I thought for the first time what fun it was to have a man at your mercy and being so in control.

This pattern did not stop there. Every night after shift Mark would let himself into my room and climb into bed with me. He had two stipulations, firstly I had to be dressed as a school girl and secondly I had to shave off all body hair and my head hair had to be in bunches or plaits. It became a nightly occurrence, finishing shift, dressing up and going to bed, and allowing Mark to wake me up, have sex and then he would leave.

After a while we didn't kiss or cuddle, we just had sex. Sometimes it was desperate and urgent, rough and to the point, sometimes he would last for what seemed like forever and after a long time he would make me suck him off. All I wanted to do was sleep, so I did what it took to get it over and done with.

Sarah's Story: **Oh Lordy**

Over the Christmas, I opted to work through and not go home. On Christmas Day, the staff from the Castle and Inn got together for one long drink fest up at the Castle with a running buffet thrown in. I mentioned to the Lord that I would like to move out of the Inn and into one of the village houses.

I had got sick of my sleep being interrupted by Mark, and when I had told him to lay off he told me that he could fire me anytime. I thought leaving the Inn would be better in that Mark couldn't just impose on me and sex would be less frequent to keep my job.

The Lord called me into his den where he was pouring out two new decanters of whisky.

"If I get you into a cottage, what would you do for me?" he said not looking at me.

"I can work some extra shifts."

"I was thinking more about how much it was worth to you and what you would do for me personally?"

"Whatever you want," I said, "I just want to get some space."

I joined the rest of the party and drank quite a lot. As people tailed off back to their rooms, or back to the Inn I stayed, very drunk, with the Italian builders and the Lord.

"Sarah, want to give me a hand taking these bottles downstairs?" I jumped up to help out. I went into the cellar, which was huge and well laid out.

The Lord came up close to me, I could smell whisky. I hated whisky.

"I don't really like girls unless they are a darn site prettier than you, but I will make the exception, let me fuck you and you can have the cottage tomorrow." He slurred most of this.

The thought of him near me made me recoil. He stank of whisky and stale rank breath and there was just something about him that made me feel sick.

However, if all I had to do was screw him to get out of the hotel, it was no worse than what the guys had done to me at the back of the club.

"Sure!"

He went to the large oak doors that lead into the cellar, shut them and turned the key. I felt quite panicky and trapped. Quite scared.

He came up to me and pulled my t-shirt over my head. I felt exposed and uncomfortable. He then undressed me slowly, rubbing his hands over me and I just shut my eyes and kept swallowing to keep the rising sick down.

Everything was horrible, the way he touched me, the way he bit into my skin hurt, the way he pinched my nipples hurt, like it was nasty. He was less than gentle as he entered me and held me far too tightly. I was as still as I could be just hoping it would be over soon. In my mind I knew nothing bad was going to happen and it would soon be over and I would get out of the hotel.

It wasn't over quickly. He took forever, my bones against the hard floor hurt and I was sore where he had bitten and pinched me. I was going to be very bruised. After what seemed like eternity he finished and got up.

"Come and see me at 2pm tomorrow, you can have the keys to the Thatch. I trust your discretion here."

The Thatch was a tiny cottage at the edge of the castle grounds, secluded from the village and totally self-contained. It was a one roomed cottage with a double bed, a place for a sofa, its own kitchen and bathroom. It was the most sought after place in the village; I didn't even know it was vacant. To get that made the last two hours bearable.

I told Mark the next day. He said quite coldly. "You are now live-out staff, so you will have to take your meals yourself. I will arrange for the salary to reflect this, I hope Sarah, and that we can continue with our special times. I will miss you."

I mumbled that it was fine and I went to see the Lord at 2pm for the keys. He was delighted to see me and was behaving as though nothing had happened.

He chucked me the keys and said, "All bills are included. Help yourself from the Castle Kitchen to anything you need. Peter the head chef has a pass key for you, if you need domestic things see Rita, she will sort you out."

I went straight to The Thatch and was delighted with what I found.

The space was lovely. I called it the Gingerbread House as it was just so sweet. Inside it was very simple, a double bed, an old wrought iron one. There was no bedding. There was a little kitchen with a sink with a window overlooking the little graveyard and a bathroom with an old free standing claw footed bath. I went over to Rita and got all the sheets and blankets and collected my staff pass key from Peter. As I was making the bed, an Australian lady came in, she looked in her early twenties and she looked like she had been crying.

"Sorry to disturb you, I've just come for the rest of my things." She indicated to a rucksack that I had not noticed.

"So you are the Lord's new screw then?" she asked casually

"I... I er don't know what you mean."

"Sure you do. Everyone knows you only get the Thatch when you're screwing the Lord."

"I'm not," I lied. "He's repulsive."

"Alright, if you wanna kid yourself, hen, but you will be booted out the moment he gets another plaything, I'm back up at the castle to make way for you."

I must have looked shocked

"How old are you?" she then asked.

"I'm seventeen."

"Shucks, you look younger; we are all talking about the kid he's screwing."

"Look it was once, alright, and it's not happening again." I shuddered.

She laughed, "Sure."

She flicked her hair back. "When you get the presents and the bonus payments it won't stop, until he wants it to, and if you end it you will be out of the village without even saying goodbyes. Ask anyone who has been around long enough."

"I'm sorry?"

"What are you sorry for? Not for me I hope, I just milk tossers like him for what I can get and move on, looks like you're doing the same."

I couldn't understand how it had come to this I felt dirty and cheap. I sat on the bed and started to think about home and how nice it would be to just be like a regular kid, going home and just enjoying college.

It was bad enough studying just theory. I had to quit all performance modules as the tube incubation had damaged my vocal chords and voice projection left me husky. Whilst I could hit notes I couldn't hold them. For the first time I wished I was still able to perform and that I was back under Jo's watchful eye. It sometimes just all felt so lonely.

The low mood stayed with me all day. I worked my shift at the Inn and Mark was cool and deliberate making me polish silver and then go on wash up after service. He knew how much I hated both. I just got on with it in my own quiet way. I could feel myself becoming overcome with strong emotional torrents again, dragging me down.

That night I took the fruit knife I had taken from the kitchen and dug it into my thigh until I could bear it no more. I then drank from the brandy bottle until I couldn't feel the pain in my head or thigh.

I assume I drank until I passed out.

Sarah's Story: **The Bargain**

The following morning I had to bin the sheets there was so much blood. I felt dreadful. It was also Saturday and a long day ahead. Still the scales had dropped and that was fine by me. I started the shift but felt so ill, Jane called me to the office.

She was offering tea and sympathy and was concerned about my weight. She put her arms round me and was trying to offer help but I felt racked with guilt and couldn't accept anything off her. She told me to take the rest of the day off and asked me to join her and Mark for dinner. I explained I couldn't, she clearly didn't understand and I could see I was hurting her feelings. I went back to the cottage and curled up in my newly made bed.

I awoke at 4pm to the door being knocked. I got out of bed and opened the door to see Jane with a tray all made up.

"Your favourite, veggie soup with loads of crusty bread, and homemade flapjack." she came in and put the tray down.

"Sarah, I am really quite concerned about your welfare, you seem to be getting thinner and it's affecting your work. You seem so distant."

"I'm sorry. I need to eat more, just some college pressure."

"Sarah I think you are drinking a bit too much as well. I would rather you come back to the Inn and stay closer to us. This is too isolated for you."

"I like it here, I want to be alone."

"Miss Greta Garbo, alone is not good." she smiled at me. I hung my head, I felt ashamed. I couldn't bear it if she knew about Mark.

"Now eat up and bring the tray over to the inn tomorrow night - OK?"

"OK, Boss." I smiled at her and as she left I ate the bread and soup, and fell straight back to sleep.

Her kindness gave me the boost I needed to get back into action. I started to eat again and concentrate on my studies. I got back into my routine and settled into the cottage well. I liked reading on my own and just having time to myself.

It wasn't to last. At the start of Spring I was moved over, with most of the other full time Inn staff, to be Castle staff for the spring festivities. I hated work in the Castle and the obligatory drinking after work. I hated the Lord who would touch me up whenever I was close to him. Within a few days of working under his nose, I was called to the cellar to collect the red wine. He was in there waiting for me and locked the door.

"We had a deal for the cottage and I've not been around much to take my side of the bargain."

"It was a one off," I said angrily, "let me out of here."

"Oh dear, you really have not got the game plan here have you? Let's be clear, it works like this. If you want the luxury of the Thatch, which is the nicest staff accommodation by far, then you need to be nice to me. If you don't want to be nice to me, there are plenty of boys and girls who will be. It's your call."

I had three more months to finish college. I couldn't survive without the job or the accommodation.

I let him undress me and I let him touch me I let him bite and I let him screw me. I hated every moment and I hated myself.

I spent the rest of the day in a foul mood, snapping at everyone and being utterly foul to the Italians who were trying to be so nice.

At the end of the shift, one of the Italians suggested they come to the Thatch and we get some pizza and chill out, away from the Castle. It suited me and I agreed. We watched TV, had some pizza and then they left. It felt close to normal. After that, the Italians swung by all the time, I didn't mind they were a nice bunch. One of them brought a battered old sofa into the Thatch so between us we could spread out on the bed and sofa.

The closeness between us all grew and I loved the way they would cuddle up to me. I often spent hours kissing one of them on the bed while the others watched TV and over time this also progressed to sex, a different one every night sometimes more than one of them, and I didn't care that others were in the room.

I had stopped caring about how I felt or was, I hated myself and latched onto any closeness I could because I needed it. Sex meant nothing, but the closeness meant everything. It was my new addiction and whilst I was with Italians, I ate pasta and pizza that they cooked on the hob and I put on a little weight. We drank every night vast quantities of spirits. My favourite was sloe gin that I drank neat. Most mornings, I awoke with very little memory of what I did the night before.

As I was swotting for my finals by day in the library, I was also juggling a ridiculous schedule outside of college hours and my nocturnal habits seemed to keep me in a constant exhausted state. Once my finals were out of the way, I had a huge sense of relief and took on more work in the Castle on top of the work at the Inn. I was raking it in financially, destroying myself emotionally.

The Italians left and the need for closeness lead to promiscuous behaviour with anyone. If there was no available man at the Inn or Castle, then I would call a cab into town and find one.

I had no self respect and would do anything to secure a bed mate for the night. I remembered less and less and as the nights got longer the drinking got heavier. One morning I woke up to £300 under my pillow and a note saying I was the best fuck in town. All I could recall were two older men coming back with me and both in bed with me. I could recall no detail. It frightened me. So I drank more in the day to forget the night before as well.

The constant state I was in proved so disruptive it was inevitable I would be called in to the office by Jane.

"Sarah, we have decided it's time we let you go."

"Why?"

"Your drinking, which we have spoken about, your behaviour with members of the public, which we have discussed previously, the several complaints about you."

"And?"

"Sarah, I know you have been sleeping with Mark."

"Didn't do much sleeping as my memory recalls Jane." The slap came as a piercing sound and pain.

"I should do a lot more than that Sarah, and I could say a lot more, but as a mother I happen to think you are one troubled child who needs a wake-up call and maybe this will be it, though I suspect it won't be."

"Come on Jane, another chance." I pleaded.

"It is out of the question. A cab will be here at 9am in the morning, here are your wages to date from here and the Castle and please go quietly."

I snatched the money and left. Mark was coming in as I walked out.

"Better tell Jane you never used anything and you never bothered to check my HIV status, which for the record is positive."

I then walked away leaving him and Jane staring at me. I didn't know my HIV status; I still had four years to wait for that.

Sarah's Story: **Home Again**

I arrived home with no warning.

My room had been given to one of my siblings and redecorated.

Mum and Dad apologised, I said I was only around for a few days. Truth was I wanted to be home for good, but time had moved on, I did not fit in anymore.

We talked about the summer and exams and I told them I thought I had passed. I also said I wanted to get away on my own.

I explained I was going to not apply for Uni until I had results, and then I may just go through clearing and decide then. No one argued.

Mum told me of her family that lived in the Highlands of Scotland but had moved, it sounded just what I wanted. Mountains and lakes.

I said that I needed time to get to know who I was. She accepted that. I explained that my results would be sent home and I would call for them.

My bank balance stood at £8,000. I had not really spent anything the past year. I took from the hotel all I wanted. My lifts into town were often combined with pickups so I had very little expenditure.

I bought a one way ticket by plane to Inverness and set off the following day. I took just a rucksack and my cash card.

Sarah's Story: **A Wee Dram**

The plane journey was traumatic, only on the basis that I had never flown before and it hurt my ears. I called the flight attendant as I thought my head was going to burst, she gave me a Fox's Glacier Mint.

The flight was under an hour and I was mesmerized about being above the clouds for the first time. It felt so strange and so surreal and I thought deeply in that one hour about just how big the world was. For the first time, I was feeling removed from the mess of the world I was living in. I felt my spirit soar and I felt freedom as we flew above the clouds.

I fleetingly recalled the moment when I was in hospital after the overdose. The bright white lights above me, and the feeling of angelic peace. I thought for a few moments about God and the universe.

That feeling of freedom made me feel different. I felt as though I was leaving everything behind and in my heart I knew I had to move forward and make a different future. No longer could I follow the self destructive path I had been taking. I had to find something else, something to make the world a more productive place to be. I had to find a future.

I think that meant I had, for the first time since the attack, decided to live.

I wanted something else. I felt old beyond my years and I felt apprehensive, but most of all I just wanted some real space to allow me to think.

I had not packed any cutting tools or scales. That was going to be behind me. On my way to the airport, I bought new leggings, jumpers, t-shirts, socks and underwear, and nothing else. I did not want anything soiled or anything that reminded me of who I was before. I bought everything in black because I had a huge hang up about the way I looked and felt black covered all.

I landed at Inverness airport and called a cab to a small village on one of the more famous Lochs. I found a B&B and asked for a room for two weeks and I paid in advance.

The lady “Mrs. McFoley-but-please-call-me Patricia” read the rules:

1. No guests in the room
2. No drinking in the room
3. To be in by 11pm unless arranged in advance
4. No Pets or Smoking
5. Snow boots to be removed in the hall

I signed to say this was fine and settled in my minimalist room. I unpacked my new clothes into the drawers and arranged my minimal things on the dresser.

I then took a walk around the village; it was just so quaint and perfect. People seemed happy. Children played and old people seemed to just sit on benches. It was quiet, there was no traffic as such and the mountains cast a picturesque backdrop to the loch. The alpine trees seemed to be painted on the backdrop and appeared somehow unreal.

I returned to the B&B at 8pm. Patricia asked if I would like to join them for a ‘wee dram’ whatever that was and I agreed.

Their lounge was cosy with old chairs and cushions, a little TV and an old table with a crocheted tablecloth, so delicate and beautiful. The room was a mixture of ornaments and photos; it felt like a home should feel.

“Meet Hamish,” Patricia said, “and settle yourself into a comfy chair.”

I held out my hand to the bearded elderly gent and said, “Hello.”

He roared with laughter and in a deep rich voice said, “Och aye lass, Hamish here is the wee Scottie, I’s Ted and yes, I’ll shake ya wee han’ though that’s rather formal, aye it is. T’would rather chink you glass o’ wee dram.”

I think I got the gist though I needed subtitles but the strong accent focused my attention.

“Well Ted,” I smiled, “we can chink when I have given this fella some attention.” The little black Scottie dog’s tail was practically propelling him upwards.

“Sit down.” growled Ted. I sat quickly.

“Not you lass, Hamish sit down and leave the wee lass.” I couldn’t help but laugh. Patricia handed me a glass a quarter full of light brown liquid, and we chinked glasses as Patricia and Ted welcomed me to their guest house and wished me a happy stay.

“This’ll put some hair on ya chest.” Ted said as he drank down his and passed his empty glass to Patricia.

I went to take a sip. I smelt the whisky, and realised to my horror what a ‘wee dram’ was. With the smell of whisky came the flashback of the cellar, of the Lord unzipping his flies and his hands on me. I shook and shivered as I recoiled at the memory.

“Are you cold lass?” Patricia said, “Here wrap a shawl round you.” She reached for one of the sofa blankets and wrapped it round my shoulders.

“You’ve not an ounce on you lass, you’ll perish on the hills in this, you mind you dress warm, it gets cold at sundown.”

I had to drink it; I could not offend these lovely people. So I took a gulp, gasping at the taste. Ted laughed, “Have you not had the taste of honey before lass?” I said I had, but none so nice.

“It’s only a Glenfiddich, it’s a common one, but we have some true drams for occasion, some single malts and some pleasant mixes. I will take you through them, given the chance.”

“I would like that,” I said.

I spent over two hours in the company of Patricia and Ted; they didn’t ask me any questions about myself. We talked about the mountains and the walks and dogs. I listened to Ted tell me about the different malts and about the history of the Lochs. I could have talked to them all night. I felt comfortable and happy in their snug little world.

I yawned, and covered my mouth apologetically and Patricia cut in saying, “You must be exhausted this being your arrival day, we shouldn’t have kept you.”

“It’s been lovely and I am sorry, tiredness has just hit me.” I said apologetically.

“There’s plenty of time for chat, and that dram has clearly taken some of the tension from your shoulders.” Patricia said, “Bed now lass and we will see you for your breakfast in the morning.”

My room was chilly; I snuggled under the crisp cotton sheets and slept as soon as my head hit the pillow.

Sarah's Story: **Soldiers**

I slept until I heard clattering in the kitchen. I had slept for ten hours without waking in sweats of panic or wondering who had been in my bed. I woke without fear, shock or surprise knowing I would be alone without a stranger in my bed next to me. As I lay there, gently waking up to the sound of Patricia humming away to herself, I was sure I could hear a distant sound of music which I feared could only be bagpipes!

I felt hungry. The pit of my stomach felt empty and I felt tempted by the smells drifting into the room. Without showering, I got dressed and went through to the dining room and saw lots of toast and pots of jams.

"I've boiled you two eggs Sarah, Ted thought you should have some protein if you are planning on a hike in the mountains today. Do you like eggs Sarah?"

I had not eaten an egg for years. I couldn't recall what an egg tasted like. "I think so." I said, noticing their rather puzzled look.

"I did you soldiers," said Patricia blushing. "You are never too old to dip soldiers into a runny egg."

Ted laughed, "Patricia you are embarrassing the wee lass, leave her be."

As Patricia bustled out, still humming, I followed Ted's actions of cutting the top off the eggs and dipping in soldiers. It tasted amazing, more than amazing, I could have screamed with pleasure at the taste. Simply delicious. I savoured every mouthful of the buttery toast and creamy egg.

"It's good to see you eat," Ted said. "We thought you looked like one of them that didn't eat."

"Shush you," Patricia snarled and then smiling at me said, "Ted's niece is one of those 'rexic' people that starve themselves, with you being a wee lass we were worried, but we can see you like your food."

She smiled and then started to frantically load the tray.

"I'm not a great eater," I said. "But I love what I do have, and those eggs were simply the best I have ever had."

Patricia looked like she would burst with pride and scuttled off back to the kitchen. Ted and I engaged in chat about a path I should take through the heather to a spot with amazing views, only about an hour's walk away. Good for a start he assured me.

I said I would be back in the evening and they wished me a happy day. As I walked, I noticed I had a little spring in my stride and a smile on my face and a carefree feeling.

I walked out of the village and followed the path Ted had told me about. It led through some gates and fields and then started to climb. I walked through heather rich in purple, pinks and yellow and took in the stunning scenery, stopping every now and then to take in the view and contemplate the beauty. It took me nearly two hours to reach the top of the, comparatively small hill. The views at the top took my breath away and I felt like Julie Andrews wanting to skip with the mountains as a backdrop to this lush green place.

I sat down in a patch of rich grass and just stared up to the mountains and down to another loch. This one was as still as glass reflecting a mirror image of the firs that filled the hillside.

I sat for two hours. I wasn't thinking, I emptying my mind without thinking, I was just void. No emotion, no feelings, nothing. I couldn't think a thought. I just sat still looking and taking in the surroundings. I walked a little further and sat again. Not thinking about anything. When you sit and open your heart, and two hours pass you by, you know your soul has left your body, momentarily. Unconsciously. You don't know where it has been, why or how, but you know two hours have passed and that you have not been aware in conscious form.

I walked back to the village and bought some rice crackers. I ate a few on my way back to the B&B.

That evening I spent an hour having a 'wee dram' before retiring to another long night's sleep. This was a sleep so deep that I recalled nothing when I woke the next day.

That first week I did the same thing every day. Each day started with two eggs and a walk to the hill. I tried a few new routes and paths and on my return I would buy something to eat. I would spend a few hours with Patricia and Ted and then retire.

At the end of my first week, I decided to go to the little shop in search of a good 'wee dram' as a gift for Ted. The man in the shop was passionate about whisky but told me he stocked the poor man's drink; however he could get me something special. I had learned a little from Ted and knew I wanted an Oban or twenty year old single malt. I also knew it would cost. I gave the man in the shop £50, which was quite a lot then, and said for him to get something very special.

The following evening, on my return, he was looking out for me. He was proud as he took me to the little back room in the shop and took out of a wooden box a bottle of quite pale liqueur.

"Ted will love this," he said.

I asked if I owed him anything and he took out some money, "No Lass, there is some change."

I instructed him to keep it for his trouble. He thanked me and said, "I can't take that missy."

I insisted so he gave me a lump of something heavy in my bag. I looked perplexed.

"Haggis," he said. "Just give it Patsy, she'll cook it a treat for you." I thanked him and left.

Ted was radiant and taken aback when I presented him, with my thanks for his maps and advice of the hills, with the 'wee dram'. He had a tear in his eye.

"Lassie this is mighty generous of you," he said, giving me a hug that felt so lovely that even my eyes filled with tears. We held each other for a few moments.

In those few moments, I felt Love. A true genuine affection in a spontaneous gesture that warmed my heart through.

Ted insisted that I join them for dinner the next night and Patricia had said she would cook the haggis and serve it with 'neeps' which I understood to be turnips. The thought didn't make me feel over the moon, but I could not refuse their hospitality.

The following night Ted opened the bottle and poured us all a generous measure. It tasted divine and nothing like the stuff we had been drinking. This was smooth, less angry on the taste buds and you could feel its calming effect as soon as it was swallowed. Now I understood why Ted called it honey.

Towards the end of the second week I asked if I may stay a further fortnight. They seemed delighted at the idea. I again paid up front. They were so trusting of me. They knew nothing about me, not even my surname, where I was from, what I was doing, but they opened up their home in more than a

B&B way and made me utterly welcome. In the short time I had been there, my cheeks looked rosy. I had a healthier glow to me, and I had no scabby marks on my body. I took only a shower every other day so as not to look at myself and, fortunately, there were no long mirrors. The absence of scales meant I was unaware of my weight, but I was only slightly apprehensive about it.

Sarah's Story: **Meeting JJ**

What I loved was the space and peacefulness on the hills and every day I felt better. I felt like part of who I was coming back into the forefront, and the irrational emotional part of me becoming more distant. I can't say what I thought about on the hills, because I am sure I didn't think, but I let my brain make order and allowed myself time to relax and unwind and feel safe. Hours could pass with no conscious thought. I believe my soul was taking a break, taking time to digest and heal.

I had noticed a grey haired lady, possibly in her late thirties on the hillside, also sitting, just like I, staring endlessly into space. We smiled and said hello a few times. This day however, I felt compelled to walk over to her. I got a few metres from her and felt the need to be silent. I sat by her. She had been crying.

We sat for several hours not speaking. Sometimes laying down, sometimes picking grass and threading it, sometimes doing nothing.

"Do you believe in God?" she said suddenly.

"Me?" I questioned. She nodded.

"I don't know, I guess so, in some form," I said.

We were quiet for a while until she said, "It's the only way isn't it? You know, to justify the bad things that happen to good people."

I wasn't sure I understood and said so.

She continued. "We must be here for a reason. Or what is the point? I think I believe that we are all part of the same spirit. We are all fragments of the Spirit of God trying to find our way back to him. I think that as we make the journey we sometimes have to come here, in a physical state, where time is slowed down so we have time to think and live by our actions. When we die, our bodies die, our soul carries on, and the closer to God we get the more we progress.

This is why there are angels to guide us, for those who are struggling, and I guess sometimes we need to learn the hard stuff and that's why we are here, to learn something so we can progress."

I said nothing. I didn't know what to think.

She asked, "Why else are we here, what is the point of it all?"

"I think," I said unsurely, "I think you may be right, but I am not really sure what I think."

We said nothing more other than goodbye as she left. That's how I met JJ.

Sarah's Story: **Giving**

I met JJ everyday in the same place for a few more days, even though I didn't know her name or anything about her. She seemed so sad and in her own space.

We said hello, and sometimes sat near each other, respecting each other's space, and then we said goodbye. Even on days where we didn't speak, I was happy in my own space while she seemed unhappy in hers. Our physical company meant we were not lonely, our souls elsewhere. Hours passed by without word.

It was a Friday morning when I walked to the same spot overlooking the loch and saw her already there. Despite it being before 9am, I could tell something was really wrong because she looked almost white and her eyes were red and swollen, and I knew I had to say something. I walked over to her.

"You are not OK?"

"No."

"Can I help?"

"No."

"Want to talk about?"

"No."

"OK."

I sat by her, I saw tears falling silently. I put my arms around her, she didn't object. She started to cry and I felt helpless. I held her tighter but said nothing. I don't know why but I kissed her forehead and told her I was there.

It seemed odd as she seemed twice my age and I had never been in the role of being the one who cared before. Over the last few years I'd become void of any external emotion, yet here I felt more love for someone else than I could ever recall feeling before.

She stopped crying after a while and lay back on the grass. I held her hand and lay back too. We must have laid in silence for an hour before she said, "Who are you?"

"I'm called Sarah," I replied. To answer who I was, was impossible.

"I'm Jennifer-Jayne but call me JJ, I'm sorry about that, just now," she blushed, her face still white.

"Do you want to talk about it?" I asked

"Not really, but you deserve an explanation," she looked me straight in the eyes. "My husband was fit and healthy up until three weeks ago, when he fainted on the rig. His dizziness was so severe he came back to the mainland where he was taken to hospital for tests and finally he had a brain scan, which revealed a huge tumour. He fell into an unconscious state prior to them operating. They operated two days ago but he still hasn't come round..."

Her voice was shaking so badly I wanted to hold her but she seemed to be taking courage to talk from somewhere so I didn't.

"He may never come round. I love him so much, I can't imagine, I can't bear the thought..."

Her tears were falling and I took her hands and said, "I'm so sorry."

"It's the children Charlotte, Emma and Tess. I can't tell them, they know their Papa is in hospital but nothing more. They are with my parents, but they come back tomorrow because my Mam's not a well woman and can't look after three young girls as my father is recovering from a stroke. It's not fair on them."

I squeezed her hands tight as she continued, "I just don't know how I am going to cope. I have extended leave from work but there is no money to hire a sitter everyday and they can't see me like this. I come here asking God for help, asking God to make Bill better and praying that the angels will help me and show me the way."

I hugged her, but I didn't know what to say, so I said nothing.

"Sarah, will you stay a while with me?" I nodded. We lay back on the grass once again in our own worlds.

All I could think of was this was real life. JJ had given me a glimpse into the real world, where bad things happen to seemingly good people. Unlike me, JJ couldn't run away as she had dependent children. There was no way out. Yet she wasn't thinking of jumping off the edge of the mountain, she wasn't cutting herself to deal with the pain, or starving herself or overdosing. She was trying to find her way through. I felt selfish.

This Bill clearly had a devoted family who adored him and I am sure he wanted to live, and his wife clearly loved him so much. Who the hell was I thinking I could throw away my life when someone was battling for theirs?

I felt uncomfortable in my thoughts. I had blocked out emotional feeling for a few weeks now, but this was making me feel again, and in feeling again, the flooding air of emotional anxiety came to the forefront of my mind. The world that I had selfishly indulged in seemed pathetic. I could feel the self hatred building in me and the urge to cut into myself was rising. I needed to feel pain again, my emotions were so strong I needed to feel something. The frustration building inside welled up tears and I blinked them away feeling even angrier with myself. How dare I cry when my pain was irrespective next to this woman's? I was so selfish.

I felt there were two of me battling for control. The emotionally "woe is me I need you to care" and the caring person with humility.

"JJ, can I do anything?" I said.

"No, Sarah, it's OK, I'll manage."

A while later she stood up and said goodbye. I said goodbye back. I felt inadequate. I needed to do something, I should have said something, but I couldn't pull myself together to deal with this properly.

I sat until the sun started to come down, so it was 9pm'ish, and by the time I had walked to the village darkness was creeping in and the shop was closing.

"You're late tonight missy," the shopkeeper said.

"I've been walking," I said. "Lost track of time."

"Ted came in looking for you."

"Oh?"

"He was worried a little, not that he will say as much. Ted's a great chap, soil of the earth and knows everyone. He seems to have a soft spot for you."

Pervert, I thought, then felt instantly ashamed.

The shopkeeper started to put an advert in the window. I was curious.

"Looking for a job eh Missy?"

"Not at all," I said.

"This is for a child minder for a week, the McEnly children. Their father's in hospital right now, sad case; we have had prayers at St Steven's all week."

"It couldn't be," I thought.

"Did JJ bring the ad in?" I asked.

"Why yes, lass, I didn't think you knew anyone."

"I don't, not really. Tell me, where does JJ live?"

"The old farm cottage on the end of the village, past Teds t'end of road, take the track to the right and it's Cottage Six, The Brambles. It's got a white door and pale blue shutters."

"Thanks. Oh, I think you can take the advert out."

I was not sure what I was doing, I was caught in the moment. I went to the B&B.

"Ted, Patricia," I said bursting into their lounge, which uninvited was terribly rude of me. They looked up from their nightly drams and paper reading.

"Sarah lass, you are later than normal; we were worried you had got yourself lost up there." said Ted.

"Sarah, are you hungry?" said Patricia.

"Yes," I said, unthinking, "but I have to go somewhere, and I may be later than eleven back and I thought I should tell you, ask you, please may I take a key as I don't want to wake you? I'm sorry I-"

"Steady lass, the words need time to come out," Ted said. "Where are you off to, it's late, it's past ten?"

"I am going to see JJ, and-"

"Very well Sarah," said Patricia. "Will you take something for me?"

"Yes of course."

I followed Patricia to the kitchen where she had wrapped a quiche and a salad on a plate.

Without saying anything, I knew that they knew about her circumstances and it seemed Patricia knew that I knew. I was pleased she didn't ask me why I was going so late, but she seemed OK with it.

I found the house, glad of the torch as night had fallen quickly as was usual in the glen. There was a lamp on in the cottage and I could see the outline of someone. I knocked the door and JJ opened it and seemed surprised to see me. She invited me in.

"JJ, can I help with the children this week? Will you let me help? I have no experience, in fact, I am not sure I am very good with children, but I want to help you and I do not want you to pay me either, in fact I want to help you and I won't let you pay me," I blurted out.

"Sarah, no!"

"Well when I say I may not be good, I mean I will try, I have a younger brother and sister. JJ let me help with the children; I can be here in the morning so you can get back to the hospital."

"I didn't mean no to the children, I mean no, you can't do it for free," she explained.

"Then I won't do it, JJ, please let me do one thing to help you and if it doesn't work out no hard feelings." I paused for breath and then said, "So what time do you want me tomorrow?"

"The children are back at 10am and I want to get back to the ward by midday, if I can."

"Then I will see you at 10am, try to sleep JJ, you look exhausted." I left, putting the quiche on the side table.

I got back at 11pm on the dot, more by chance than planning and Ted was in his pyjamas.

"Done what you had to lass?" I nodded and he added, "The kids are bonny girls, happy girls but a handful. I take it you offered to look after the wee things?"

"How did you know Ted?"

"I know your heart Sarah and I have seen you on the mountains with Jennifer. The whole village has that family in our prayers right now. Now Patricia said you said you hadn't eaten, so there are some chicken sandwiches under a plate in the kitchen and a slice of cake, I know you eat like a bird but you will enjoy those."

"Thank you Ted and thank Patricia for me."

Ted turned the key and went upstairs. I went to the kitchen and took the food back to my room.

I surprised myself at eating it all. I had eaten my eggs and toast that morning but nothing since, so a good fifteen hours with nothing but water. I could still count my ribs and my hip bones still nicely jutted out and so I knew my weight must be steady. I decided the food would not hurt.

Sarah's Story: **The Wee Things**

The following morning I met the girls.

Lotte, Em and Tess. Lotte was eleven, Em nine and Tess was seven. They were lovely children with happy faces and lovely smiles. They asked how their Papa was and I notice JJ brush over the subject with a bland "Fine" before kissing them goodbye. She shot me a grateful grin and pushed a note in my hands. We waved her off and went back in.

The note was hurried and just pointed out where the freezer was, what the girls could eat, and noting she would be back at 5pm. The girls wanted to do activities and we settled on a walk. They also wanted a picnic. The house had minimal supplies and certainly not enough for three hungry girls' picnic so we went to the local store and bought bread and bananas and peanut butter, crisps, chocolate and apples, coca cola and cake. I made up the picnic back at their home and piled the treats into a rucksack. The girls wanted to take the low road to the edge of the loch, unsure of the path I decided to consult Ted on the way.

Ted warned me not to let the girls paddle in the loch. Its steep sides meant that just less than one metre out into the loch the depth was hundreds of metres. This is what gave the loch its black colour. I heeded his warning and stuck to the path.

Along the way, we found ourselves looking down drains for witches, up into the trees for bears, we played hide and seek. We had impromptu games of skittles and jumped over logs, we found curious things to talk about like why some leaves grow long and some grow spiky and we found a frog that we tried to catch. It was random, exciting and by the time we stopped for lunch it was gone 3pm and we were all hungry. We ate our lunch and made daisy chains and buttercup bracelets then we headed home. I was aware of the time so we played marching games to get back quicker than our journey there had been.

We got back at 6pm, I was glad I had left a note for JJ as had she come home she would have wondered where we were. JJ was not back so I ran baths for them as they were pretty grubby. At 7pm the phone rang and Lotte answered it. It was her Mum and she passed the phone to me.

"Sarah, I have only just left, I am so sorry . . ."

"Its fine JJ, I will be here when you get back, no hurry, no rush OK?"

"Thanks Sarah."

After bath time, I made them 'hedgehogs in mud' for their tea, just for fun, thinking that it was the best way to present sausage and mash which could be pretty unexciting for little girls. The girls thought it was lovely and ate it all, they were tired and ready for bed, so at 8pm I read the story of 'Beauty and the Beast' until all three of them were asleep.

JJ came back at 9pm full of apologies. I assured her it was fine and I would be back at 8am the next morning so she could get the first bus to the town.

This was the pattern we followed for two weeks. I bought shopping so I could do the children's meals and I looked after them for twelve or thirteen hour days. I always left JJ some dinner and on occasion poured her a glass of wine before I left. She didn't say much about Bill, just that he had come round and there was hope.

I had stopped thinking, pure and simple. The children wore me out. As I ate with them I had started to eat three small meals a day, and I looked forward to my 'wee dram' every evening with Patricia and Ted. I explained to Ted that the children were finding it really hard not knowing what was happening with their Papa and that I could see JJ was avoiding talking about it.

The children would ask me about death and about dying and about heaven and hell. They would ask me about angels and the more macabre things like where a body goes and if worms ate you. They asked to go to a graveyard, which I drew the line at.

Ted said he thought they needed a few days away and that maybe he could take us camping, I thought it was a great idea and put the idea to JJ.

JJ was fine with the idea and the children were delighted with the news. We packed sleeping bags and rucksacks and Ted showed us his six-man tent with two bedrooms and our plans were fine tuned, with good weather ahead for the following week. The only thing that was worrying me was the fact I would be sharing with Ted.

That night was the first night I started to have flashbacks. I would wake thinking there was a man on top of me, I would wake with cramp in my arms where I dreamt I was being pinned down, I would wake gasping for air because in my dream someone was trying to kiss me. I would wake with the same feeling that I'd awoken with when I was in the village, not knowing who I had had sex with or how many. Not knowing what they'd done except to notice tell tale signs when I came round and not knowing if they used any protection. I would wake with the sweats and panic rising.

Worst of all, I started to think of Ted as one of those men. Would he be expecting me to sleep with him with Patricia away? I knew he had a soft spot. Was I supposed to sleep with him to thank him for taking the girls away? I couldn't bear the thought of it, but I couldn't cancel the trip either.

Patricia took me to one side one morning after breakfast, she said she was concerned as the last few nights she had heard me shouting out, I told her I was having some night tremors and she was sympathetic.

Sarah's Story: **It's Just Sarah**

The day before the trip, after looking after the girls all day, I poured JJ a glass of wine and went to say goodbye. She asked me to stay.

"It's been three weeks Sarah that you have been looking after the girls and everywhere I go in the village they say you are a marvel with them. The girls love you and are having so much fun, from walking, to crafts, to drama, to dance. There seems no end to the things you are doing for them, I am so grateful, but I feel so guilty. I know you are buying things because I have not got things in and I know it is costing you money and I am giving you nothing, and to be honest I am embarrassed and don't really know what to say or do."

Ouch! I did understand how JJ must be feeling. "JJ, it's fine, I love doing this..."

"But you have your life Sarah. God, I don't even know your surname..."

"It's Sarah, just Sarah."

"But who are you Sarah? Why are you here? How old are you?"

"I'm taking a break, which I saved for. I am eighteen and I am trying to figure what to do with the rest of my life, as for who I am, well I guess I am trying to find that out too."

"Eighteen, Sarah, I didn't know, that's so young, you seemed older, somehow, just, I don't know why. You shouldn't be spending your holiday picking up my mess."

"It's not a mess. It's . . . I don't know, maybe it's just meant to be."

We paused. A silence came between us and I sat down. I had to tell her something because the guilt in her face was uncomfortable.

"JJ, my life has been a mess so far. I don't want to detail anything, but I needed time on my own. I needed as long as it took to find myself and I needed to just be me, or find out who I am. I had no plans when I came here and I still don't, and I have no future until I decide what that is going to be. I have learnt something - I have learnt to give, I have learnt to feel love and how to care and I have learnt how to spot beauty again. My world had got pretty dark and intense, your children have made it simple again for me, it's not just been a pleasure but a privilege and so... so you should not feel that you need to thank me. OK?"

"You are different Sarah, different and deep and I wish I could talk to you more . . . and help you . . ."

"JJ, the last thing I want is that. Look, I don't want to talk, I don't want to discuss my life, I just want to be left to be me. How's Bill by the way?"

"Much better Sarah, there's talk of him coming home next week for a few days at a time at first and then gradually to full time. He's through the worst and on the mend."

"That's great JJ." We hugged and held each other and then I left.

The camping trip went ahead. We had three nights under canvas and Ted was a real gentleman. In the day he spent time by the lake with the children catching fish, he had a line, the children had nets. Lotte did try a line but got bored. We all collected wood in the day for the campfire that we kept going from the moment we got there. Ted made us dig a moat around the edge of the fire because it was protected forestry land and there was lots of dry wood.

The moat also stopped Tess getting too close to the fire so full marks to Ted. We collected butterflies and creepy crawlies. We collected wood that could be carved by Ted and we made a hammock out of rope and an old sheet that Em loved swinging in. We made rope swings and I indulged in the childhood fantasy just as much as the children.

The first night I boiled potatoes and heated up beans on the campfire and we made corn beef hash which everyone loved covered in HP Sauce. For something so simple, it was delicious. We washed up in the lake. By sun down at 9.30pm Tess was so tired she was falling asleep in Ted's lap and Em was struggling to stay awake. By 10pm all three children were asleep and then Ted opened a bottle of scotch and we had just one or two 'wee drams' before calling it a day.

On the first night after draining our whisky Ted said, so simply, "You need have no fear me lassy. The only thing you will have to put up with tonight is me snoring. Patricia said I am incurable."

I laughed. Ted was true to his word, not only on me having nothing to worry about, but his snoring would have kept the wild beasts at bay!

I was as sad as the children when the trip came to an end. We packed up. I longed for a bath and the children needed one. I was a little worried JJ may be shocked at the rather grubby mess her girls were in. As we got to the door, JJ came out, looking utterly radiant and said, "Girls, Papa is home, but he needs rest, so we will have dinner then it's bedtime."

She hugged the girls who were full of their adventure and I had never seen her look so happy. I went to say goodbye, but she pulled me in, "You are staying for dinner Sarah. You are not getting off that easily."

As I walked in, the children were hugging and kissing a man in the corner, he was pale and his head was bandaged still, but his dark hair was poking out and he had a handsome face. He looked a strong man.

JJ introduced me to Bill. I felt uncomfortable and intrusive on this happy, but family occasion. I did however stay for dinner and enjoyed a lovely roast dinner for the first time in four years. As JJ went to give the girls a bath, I cleared and washed up. I left without saying goodbye as I could hear the girls still chatting about their adventures.

I knew the time had come to move on.

The following morning I called Mum to open the exam results.

"Sarah, where the hell are you? What are you doing? Not a call in over two months and your exam results have been here for two weeks, you will miss clearing."

"Only if I have passed anything. I've just been busy, that's all."

"Busy doing what? What sort of attitude is that to take? Never mind, do you want me to open these?"

"Please." I heard her tear the envelope and read them.

"Two Bs and a C," and she then told me what in. I was pleased. I had enough points to go to Uni.

"So what are you going to do now Sarah? You can't flit around forever?"

"I am going to teach," I announced, not sure where that came from.

"But that's such a low paid profession. You could be doing so much more."

I let her talk, and when she was finished I said I would let her know what Uni I got into and we left it at that.

I spent much of the next week in a phone box going through clearing, filling in application forms, faxing them off at the library in town and literally draining my money on phone calls.

Finally, I had an offer from a Uni near to London and decided to take a place there. I had just two weeks before the start of term. I was too late to get into one of the Halls of Residence so I had to set to work again on the phone from Scotland calling round rooms to rent, but without any luck. In a frantic call, I called the Uni accommodation office in tears and they told me it was my lucky day as a room in one of the halls had come available. I accepted instantly.

Patricia and Ted were delighted for me. News in the village spread fast and even the shopkeeper congratulated me. JJ had popped a card in to say "Good Luck" with a note to say she would like to take me for dinner to say thanks. I called by to decline and explained that I would rather go for a picnic with the girls before I left.

It turned out that the girls went to their Grandma's for the week so JJ and I went up into the hills alone. JJ had made a picnic of fishy things and champagne, which despite my apprehension was delicious.

"Sarah, you seem happier than when we met up here eight weeks ago."

"So do you JJ."

"Have you found the answers you were looking for?"

"I feel happier JJ, I am not sure what the question was that I needed answering, but I feel better."

"Do you recall our first conversation?"

"Yes."

"I think you were the answer to my prayers Sarah."

"I think JJ, your children were the answer to mine." We smiled at each other, and we understood.

"JJ, I think life is weird, don't you?"

"Yes, but I think everything happens for a reason. Even the bad stuff happens for a reason too. It's the only way you can explain bad stuff happening to good people."

"Maybe. But what happens next JJ?"

"Next? I think our souls go on and on learning until we have learnt enough."

"What's enough?"

"Who knows Sarah? All I know is there is a bigger picture and there are angels working with us, every day, we only have to ask for help. We have to be open to The Plan and allow things to happen."

"Will Bill be OK?"

"We have had the all clear. He will be home full time next week and possibly back to work in six months. He had me worried; I thought I had lost him. We argue and we fight, especially when he is away on the rigs, and sometimes I can't wait for him to get back out there. This has bought it home to me how much I love him and how much my family means to me. I will never take it all for granted again, for as long as I live. I am determined to make up all the lost time and I am just grateful I have the chance."

I understood totally. I too had to make up for lost time and stop hiding in a veil of darkness and sadness and start living. As I sat there with JJ, the sun reflecting on the loch I knew I would never try to take my life again and I would never intentionally lose another day to bad memories. JJ was right, there were angels walking with us. Despite all the bad things that could happen, there was always someone at the critical moment to turn things round and help.

I was sad to leave Scotland and this little village. I had been there for three months and was officially the longest lodger Ted and Patricia had ever had. I was sad to say goodbye to the children and JJ, and we vowed to write to each other.

I was walking away a different person to the one who had arrived. This time when the plane soared over the clouds, I knew there was a God and I sent my thanks to him.

Now: **Susannah**

It was Susannah who made Sarah realise that children are indeed, wonderful healers.

Sarah confided that she had never thought too much of what the trip to Scotland had meant, but the short time in which she was there it was the normality, the innocence and the 'live for today' attitude of the children that transformed her outlook.

Sarah was still trying to get to grips with why Susannah was having such a profound effect on her. As for understanding the torrent of feelings for her, for Sarah it was impossible.

I suggested that maybe these things are not meant to be understood.

Sarah has told Susannah that she is in love with her. Susannah understood and was not fazed. Sarah told her she thought she may have a crush on her, Susannah gave her a hug and understood, and Sarah told her she thought she may be a Mother Figure, and Susannah understands.

Sarah has told me that she doesn't understand her feelings, and yet Susannah understands and has no expectations. Susannah just tells Sarah that in time it will work itself out and that in time she will be nothing more than a memory, and the importance of her in Sarah's life will vanish.

Susannah is perpetually gentle, in words, in actions and in dealing with matters of the heart. I see the way in which she handles Sarah and cannot help but think her soul must be terribly advanced to have a heart filled with such love and compassion. The world sometimes feels so full of loud people all shouting to be heard, not realising it's the gentleness of a calm voice that can be heard over them all.

Sarah's Story: **Home**

I arrived home a fair bit heavier but a lot healthier in body and mind than when I had left.

Mum seemed genuinely pleased to see me and both Mum and Dad were both pleased that I had signed up to a degree with teaching status.

I had only allowed myself a stay of one night, which turned out to be plenty. It was a nice stay in which I sorted out the last of my belongings at home. Most things had been boxed and my siblings had taken over. It was nice to unpack the boxes, dumping the childhood items that had been left untouched for several years and packing items that were left to take to Uni.

I weighed eight stone exactly. No one made comment to this, but wearing leggings for three months I had not really taken much noticed of my expanding waistline. I was still a size ten and moderately happy with this. I did however ditch the leggings for a purchase of several pairs of Levis. I made a vow of staying a ten so they would fit.

My savings had dropped down to just over £5000 and I wanted to keep that to buy a small car and take my driving test so set was I on finding work from day one at Uni.

Mum and Dad for the first time gave me a gift of money. They gave me £500 per term for the course duration to be paid on the first of each term. This was towards the cost of study, but I also knew it was insufficient. I was however grateful.

I left with my same old rucksack and large sports bag and I was driven to the train station where I said goodbye to Mum and Dad. They both gave me big hugs and said that, whilst they didn't say it very often they were very proud of me and relieved to see me healthy and happy. They wished me lots of luck as they waved me off.

It felt almost normal, but also a little sad. The view of my parents being utterly detached from me seemed a little unfair, but then I couldn't let twenty-four hours change four years. They said I was welcome to come home in any breaks and they would look forward to it and I said I would come home, but deep inside I knew I probably would find work in the breaks.

Sarah's Story: **Wild Times**

The process of enrolling at uni meant two things:

1) Endless queues of Freshers asking, "So what are you studying / what 'A' levels did you do?"

2) Endless over-enthusiastic Student Union people trying to sell me events.

In the end I took up residence in the bar.

The student bar is the cheapest place on earth. A whole pound for a pint or double. Conscious of the tight fitting Levi's, for me it was a double and ice no mixer.

First night I got lost. I recall drunkenly falling in a bush and deciding as it was fairly warm it would be a fine place to sleep. Alas a security man woke me and made me turf out all bags and pockets before finding my room keys and ensuring I was escorted back to my room and put to bed.

The following morning, as I rejoined the endless queues, loads of people talked to me about a great night in the bar. As my memory was hazy, I found myself just asking about their 'A' levels and chosen course. Sad.

By lunchtime, vodka on the rocks sounded better than another bloody queue so I went to the bar to be greeted like one of the troops. The bar man, who ran the bar employed by the Uni said, "The job's yours if you want it."

Hastily I ransacked my memory banks and could hazily remember me asking for a job. I also recall the rounds of slammers and dancing on the bar to 'American Pie' whilst flirting outrageously.

"Yep, I want it," I said. "When do you want me is the question?" I openly flirted.

"Oh every night, twice a night," he grinned joining in with the 'double entendres'.

Rachel, who was on the Students Union and a 3rd year, slapped him on the head. "Leave off the fresher Terrance!" she said to a round of laughter.

Terrance was a middle aged man who was also an Environmental Science Lecturer. He oversaw the running of the bar and had done since the previous bar man the year before had suddenly dropped down dead. The Uni were trying to recruit a new bar manager but, in the interim, Terrance had stood in as running pubs was a family business and he knew his stuff. He did however leave it generally to a mix of students to do all the hard work. Terrance was a little pervy in my opinion and could certainly be public in his admiration of the female anatomy. He apparently had a wife and kids in Dorset, but no one seemed totally sure of this.

"Alright Sarah, how does every weeknight sound?"

"Surely weekends are busier," I said.

"Sure, but I have lots of my old faithfuls in then, it's the weeknights I need staff."

"Suits me, it's a deal," I said giving a 'high five'.

"Drinks on me then," said Terrance, handing me double, neat vodka.

By the end of the first week I could understand why it was dubbed 'Fuck a fresher week' by anyone who knew Uni life. Had I have wanted to I could have slept, no; let's say screwed anyone, any and every night of the week if not more than once. Reckless drinking from several idiots who had never left mum (or home before) and total freedom meant that you could do anything. I had rejected snorting coke from the after bar drinks club that occurred after Terrance had left. I only pretended to smoke a joint so to not look un-cool and certainly drank well above my natural tolerance level.

I didn't have sex, though the option was there if I wanted it. I did take part in the stripping of at least four male students and teasing them to the point of no return. I was dubbed a hard chick by everyone that met me.

A job in the bar had a kudos I didn't expect and my hardened air was seemingly attractive to both girl and boy students. It raised my profile to a popularity level I had never experienced before. For the first time in my life, I was making friends and having a laugh without disrespecting my body too much.

Lectures went well. I learnt that my photographic, yet dyslexic, memory was proving a lifesaver. I could recall parrot fashion huge chunks of text using the same visual approach I had previously used to learn lines. This meant studying came naturally and easily, and whilst I was normally recovering from the event of the night before, my memory recall in lectures was still better than most sober students.

The elections for the student union came up. I had been nominated for Halls Counsellor. Not on merit but bar popularity. I won. I was promptly upgraded to a two double bedroom apartment in Halls. It was luxury. Terrance even popped along to fit six optics above my bed as a flat warming present.

In no time at all, all the good parties were in my room. Mostly all night and mostly alcohol and drug fuelled.

I prepared each night after lectures and before work in the bar with a mirror for cutting lines of coke, paper razzes for rolling joints. My optics were full of premium brand spirits. Sex was always on the agenda, in that couples would share the spare bed, two or four at a time and my bed was usually for chat but couples fell into each other as drugs and alcohol took effect. The music was never my personal taste but whatever was cool at the time. Black Sabbath, Ozzy and Motown were the norm. As drink took effect, I preferred a bit of the Nolan's, Abba and Kylie which I think everyone else secretly liked really. When you are drunk, it becomes almost cool to be uncool!

I would give blow jobs on request if I felt like it, but would never have sex. I mostly walked around in just a basque to tease. I had an air of authority and I used it. The party was mine and I was the boss. It was a power I manipulated. Peace and love I could deal with, but any negativity and it was game over.

I was quite manic. I was either in control and as high as a kite or depressed. Still, no one noticed.

If anyone misbehaved on the party scene, me and my bar pals would not serve them and we left them waiting endlessly at the bar until they got someone else to get the drinks in. It was my way of humiliating them for breaking my rules. Word got out about my nightly parties and all the world, it seemed, wanted to be my friend. I never did drugs and wasn't tempted, and whilst I would drink, I knew where the line was. Even when rolling drunk, I still knew when to draw the line between flirting and letting anyone touch.

I openly admitted I was a tease and was quite firm with my 'Look but don't touch' motto. I was in control and it would stay that way.

The whole of the first year carried on like this. I got the best shifts at the bar and the student bar and I became almost synonymous. I also took free alcohol and £900 a month tax free. I got all the promotional stuff, from tons of condoms to bean bags, which just added to the party palace that my room had become.

I studied hard by day, often on four hours sleep. I would do all my work in the library in free periods and got good grades with every assignment. However, I frequently fell asleep in lectures and a few times still felt drunk and hazy the following day.

Hazy days and lazy ways.

Then: **Toxic Shock**

At the end of the first year, I got a job on both reception and on campus security for the summer. I was the first female security guard ever hired. My reputation went before me I think as I was known to work and party hard. Even so, I knew the old security guys saw me as a laughing stock.

It took four weeks of twelve hour shifts on a rota that included nights for them to soften towards me. The banter saw me eventually as 'one of the lads' and I openly flirted with the men even though they were all married and twice or three times my age. By the end of the holidays, I had netted over 6K and booked myself on to a two week crash driving course after which I passed first time. I bought myself a Mini and felt even happier to have a new degree of freedom. This was especially useful as my teaching practice was coming up in the second year at local schools and I didn't want to have to rely on public transport.

So having not drank all summer, the return to the Freshers' Week was about to test me.

I still had the same Hall's status, but this time I was Floor Mother to the first years and Woman's Officer on the Student Union. Elections were run purely on a popularity basis and any actual credentials for the roles were irrelevant.

I enjoyed being on the Student Union with the added kudos this bought, along with working on the bar. It meant that friends came easily. The perks were just fantastic. Most of the time a Floor Mother was only needed for the odd one or two really shy girls who were missing home at the start of term. Being 'Floor Mother' did mean I had to make sure the communal bathrooms were kept clean, and that the lads cleaned the bath out after them, the loo was being flushed, the kitchen kept within minimum hygiene standards for the good of all. I never had any trouble from anyone in this respect. I was either blessed with tidy students or ones that didn't wash or eat. For first year students, it was impossible to tell which.

My role of Woman's Officer was a little more daunting. Thankfully there were two of us to deal with the multitude of women's issues and represent women at the Uni.

Freshers' Week sees all the large companies promoting their brands. Crates of sanitary towels and tampons arrived for my attention, as did mountains of Durex and even the new female condom, which got lots of laughs. I was expected to support the awareness of Toxic Shock Syndrome cases caused by tampons as my first remit. Thank goodness I was popular and sticking signs up on all the lav doors about TSS was fast getting me a reputation and I did not want to be nicknamed the tampon woman.

During Freshers' Week I also had to issue rape alarms to all the female students, which was a mission and a half. Little things that you pull a pin out of that screech loud enough to break glass. Everyone was cynical about them, and a few girls wanted to know if there was an alarm to attract men, as repelling them was not their idea of fun.

So Freshers' Week I spent most of the time walking, from hall to hall, with boxes of sanitary towels, tampons, rape alarms and condoms. Towards the end of the week, I decided to set up a free shop in the bar. We all wore tampons as earrings, made hats out of towels and blew up the condoms. Prizes were given to the largest inflated condom and the most innovative thing to do with a tampon.

After a week of caring and sharing Woman's Officer duties, and with fresher parties starting in earnest, I decided to join in and stop being all responsible.

Most nights the parties started at midnight when I got back from the bar. Terrance would always sneak me a bottle or two to add to my now twenty-four optics. People would show up and, whilst the music would stop at 2am, we were still playing games like 'Spin the Bottle' and 'Strip Poker' until 4am, if not right through to dawn.

Sex was open, free and easy. If the bottle said have sex with someone, off you went to my spare bed. This is what made the parties exclusive and popular.

Feeling more comfortable with this open format, I joined in fully and decided I may as well have sex too.

Orgies were common; it resulted in too many same answers on 'Spin the Bottle'. We had only one rule. Join in after a shower. So most people showered together and then joined in. I slept with anyone but on my terms. I was Queen Bee and was seen as 'hard to pull' and a 'desirable shag'.

It bought kudos to those I had sex with the night before and they hung at the bar waiting for me, usually only to be humiliated as I really didn't care. I enjoyed crushing them and flirting with the next conquest. To me it was a game. I didn't really care about the consequences. A few would call me a prick tease and to me that just made me harder, pointing out if they couldn't get me they obviously were not good enough.

I was cruel and mean. I used men and treated them like dirt the following morning. I laughed in their faces and after shagging them would ridicule them in public; I liked watching them crumble. I had power and kudos and I used it. Rather than deter them, they seemed to always want to come back for more.

Back in my room, the air was one of "anything goes". In the first few weeks of the new term a rather butch girl who was an out and proud lesbian saw me as a challenge and as she fitted well into the cliques that hung around the bar joined in the fun back in my room. She was my first lesbian encounter and she took me by surprise when she kissed me the first time. She was quite physical and I liked the way she took charge of me, what I liked even more was the affect it had on the males around me. Clearly our public displays were a turn on for them and I openly flirted with her too. My reputation was still the same but the "swinging both ways" rumour just seemed to add to my popularity.

People often stayed over and we would wake after falling asleep on each other, or rather, passing out on each other. It became an unwritten rule that you had to have a 'hair of the dog' before leaving. With the optics set above my bed, it was a case of lie back and drink for England.

Sarah's Story: **Another 'Slap'**

I don't recall eating much but my weight had gone up from seven stone to seven and a half. Most if not all of my calories came from alcohol and the only food I recall eating was toast with marmite. I would go weeks without a proper meal just snacking on crisps in the bar.

I cut my long hair to a more respectable and tidy arrangement and got rid of the schoolgirl plaits I often wore. I had taken to dressing most evenings like a school girl with white shirt, black mini and stockings as it was part of my teasing. The ponytail or plaits added to the innocence, but was hard to maintain so I had it cut in a razor sharp bob that suited me more. I had two chunks of bright red put in and at the same time had my ears pierced several times and got a nose stud.

The new look was more streetwise than schoolgirl and seemed more me, hard and detached and unapproachable.

I still studied hard and, despite being up most of the night, I was shocked when my key lecturer booked me in for an appointment to see her. It was quite rare to be called to see your personal lecturer; I was nervous and racked my brain to understand why I had been called. My essay grades were OK; my performances were moderate and acceptable although I wasn't giving it my best. The childcare studies were OK even though I found the modules on childcare history hideously boring and the social side of it mind numbingly so. That said, my essays were coming back passable.

I felt sick to the stomach as I waited outside her room. I had knocked and been told to wait. The waiting was making me nervous.

"Come in Sarah." I went into her room which was covered in theatre posters from West End shows and classical opera. She was there with the Halls Coordinator and one of the teaching staff.

"Hi Valerie." I sat on the chair in front of her. I didn't acknowledge the others.

"Sarah, do you know why I, we, have asked to see you at all?"

"No."

"Well, to put it as simply as I can, the Foundation Course tutors had a meeting last week and you were a topic of concern amongst everyone, especially on the Qualified Teaching Status side."

"Really? Why? My grades are OK." I knew what I needed to get my QTS.

"Your grades are fine Sarah. The fact you are still clearly under the influence of alcohol most of the day is not. We cannot let you start teaching practice the way you are, it would jeopardise your whole degree and the reputation of the course placement, and we are not prepared to let you into a school until you have sorted yourself out. That's if you can."

"I think this is a bit unfair Valerie."

"That's a shame Sarah, but if you got sober enough for long enough to see things from our point of view then you may just see we have a good point."

"Valerie I am fine, surely my grades tell you that?"

"You have a fine memory Sarah, and you could be doing a lot better, your grades are acceptable but you are not working anywhere close to your potential."

"But, Valerie-"

"You are here to listen, Sarah, not argue with me."

"Valerie-"

"Sarah. You have a choice. I have delayed your teaching practice until the third term when you will do four weeks to make up not doing the two weeks now.

It took a while to bring the teaching team on side with this as it steps outside normal operational procedures. As your personnel tutor, I have to look after your welfare and I actually see more in you than you are currently demonstrating. You will need to demonstrate attendance on a totally sober level."

She paused and looked at the other teaching staff in the room, seemingly for support. I saw her take a long breath before saying, "Sarah, I have researched into your student life and your activities outside academia and-"

"That's outrageous - what has that got to do with . . . ?" I protested.

"Enough Sarah! You are here to listen, not argue, it is clear that you have quite a reputation and it's almost too embarrassing to repeat some of the things that I have heard."

The Halls Coordinator spoke for the first time, "Other students have complained to me directly, as they can't complain about you to you, but the parties that go on, sometimes all night, are disruptive. There are reports of high sexual activity with people from outside of the college."

"Hold on, I think this is invading my privacy and the people in my room are all in college here . . ."

"I have no evidence, only reports from other students. I will be fully investigating the reports later, but one thing is clear the problems are arising from your room."

Valerie spoke again, "Sarah do you want to stay on your course?"

"Yes."

"Then shut up and listen." It was like receiving a slap, her tone sharp and firm and inpatient.

"You are in danger of being thrown off the course Sarah, so I advise you to listen and listen hard. I have looked into your student activities, and heard about your night time activity shall we say. I am not going to judge you Sarah, but you are wasting your talent and throwing a good future down the drain. Not to mention not having much respect for yourself, from what I have heard you are leaving yourself open to a whole range of health issues. It's hardly what a student teacher should be portraying. That said what you do in your own time is up to you. "

She looked over at the Halls lady, "However, I have spoken to the Halls Coordinator and you are to be removed as Floor Mother as you are neither approachable for a student in crisis and heaven knows what they would walk into. It's a misuse of the status and privileges given to you. You will therefore be downgraded, as of this afternoon, to a room in the Doorman's Court where you will have just a basic single room, the only one available is a smaller room, but it's that or nothing."

"Valerie this is so unfair."

Tears of anger were falling freely. Without a tissue, I was sniffing as tears and snot rolled down my face, which I tried to brush away angrily.

"Unfair it may seem, from my point of view it may just be your saving grace. The college have no jurisdiction over your bar employment, but we are asking you to reduce your shifts to a more acceptable level and have asked Terrance to support this. If money is an issue we have a hardship fund you can apply for."

"I like it Valerie, I like my job."

"Unfortunately Sarah, your tutors see how it's affecting you and whilst it is your decision, I can only advise you to quit your job. Whilst in that environment you are wasting everything I thought you wanted. This is your first, but final warning before we look at removing you from your courses, so the ball is very firmly in your court."

She handed me a tissue, but did not look sympathetic.

"Go now Sarah, you need to get your room sorted out. You can come and see me again if you want to discuss anything further. Sarah, if you want to continue your studies here you need to have a more serious approach to your work and a more studious attitude for your subjects. We expect an immediate change from you and will be reviewing your performance in two weeks time and two weeks continually there on in."

With that I was shown the door.

Sarah's Story: **In the clear**

I cried tears of self pity by the duck pond for about an hour. Thick black eyeliner staining my hollow cheeks and ruby red lipstick smudged. Eyes red with puffy cheeks I went straight to the bar.

"Bloody Hell Sarah, what the fuck's up?" Johnny seemed concerned and came over hugging me in his very gay way.

"About to be thrown off my course, is Terrance around?"

"Out back, moving frog spawn into buckets or something gross like that."

"Cheers."

I walked through the bar. Stopped, took a double measure of vodka, swallowed in one, and continued out to the back yard, where Terrance was indeed doing something odd with frog spawn.

"Jeez Sarah, you look rough." He stopped messing with the spawn, "You have been to see Valerie, I know, you're here to resign from my team of ace bar staff, yes?"

I nodded, "Guess I have no option?"

"I don't think you do Sarah but I am sorry it's happened. Maybe you need to study more, you do give a lot of your time to the bar."

"Not sure it's the bar that's the problem T, I think it's . . ."

"The partying? Yes, you are right. You are a legend Sarah, freaky, odd, ruthless, a right old tart but we do all love you, and it ain't gonna be the same without you . . ."

I started crying again and he came over and hugged me, "But we still love you and you can still come in for as many bevvies as you can deal with!"

I left after a hug and brief snog, which can't have been all that pleasant given the tears and snot. The closeness brought more tears and I had to go. I went to my room where the Halls Coordinator was waiting.

"It's a blooming mess in here Sarah, have you ever cleaned this room once?"

I shook my head, "I doubt it."

"I guess I should turn a blind eye to all this," she indicated to the pictures of erotica on the walls and the joint ends on the floor.

"Seriously, I have never done drugs, but my guests have."

"I am turning a blind eye Sarah because, as sure as God made little apples, you would be out of Uni if I report this. For what it's worth I actually feel sorry for you, for some reason escaping me, so help me get cleared up and we can all move on."

I willingly started to tidy, packing my own stuff in bin bags and filling a few others with rubbish. Ironing the floor with brown paper to lift the candle wax stains off the carpet and cleaning the windows that had been painted. I scrubbed the walls and bathroom and within four hours the room seemed habitable.

"You are going to get charged for some damage Sarah, mostly the candle wax, didn't you read the rules?"

"I don't really do rules," I said, "But whatever the bill, it's fine."

With that she handed me a new key, "Your new room. Take better care of it."

I went to Doorman's Court, known for its poky dingy rooms, and found it was worse than its reputation. The room had a single bed, I couldn't recall the last time I had slept in a single bed, and a desk and lamp and that was it. It had one window and the heavy trees outside let in little light. It was grim. I unpacked my PC, books and paper and made the bed.

Utterly depressed, I decided the best thing was to go to bed. I had a half bottle of vodka and despite it being five in the afternoon I swigged it from the bottle and cried myself to sleep, indulging in the self pity of emotion.

The following morning I awoke with a dry throat and the shakes. I drank the water out of the tap in the room, and felt better but the shakes did not ease. I felt sick and I was sweaty and I knew I must be sickening for something.

I went to the morning lectures, people commented on how pale I was. I went to the canteen and ordered chips and a hamburger, something that would normally repulse me but I needed to eat to stop the shakes. It helped, but I still felt ill. I went to bed at 6pm and slept through to 8am the following morning, waking once again in a sweat and shaking almost uncontrollably. I ate toast and had coffee and did the days lectures, I felt poorly and unable to stop the shaking and nausea. The following day was even worse, I had been awake all night feeling sick, sweating and shaking. At 4am I called the Uni nurse.

Concerned by my weight, colour and state, she called an ambulance that took me to London Hospital and sat with me through check in and tests. A sedative put me to sleep and when I awoke I was surprised to see Valerie at my side.

As I came round, she told me I had severe alcohol poisoning and the DT's (detoxification), and that my physical symptoms were that of an alcoholic going 'cold turkey'. I could see she was not sympathetic, being called out for something self- inflicted, but I could tell she was concerned.

"I didn't realize you were this bad Sarah, can I call your parents?"

"No!"

"Is there something you want to tell me?"

"Nope."

"Something must be behind all of this . . ."

"No, there isn't."

"I am here if there is."

"OK."

"They are keeping you in for a few days Sarah, I will come again," She upped and left.

I felt ill. Really ill. I had a drip, and perpetual hangover. I was being given five meals a day and I felt exhausted so slept pretty much constantly. No one came to see me except Valerie, which sort of surprised me. I was expecting half the bar to turn up.

I put on eight pounds in one week. I was severely dehydrated and lacking in vitamins and the withdrawal from alcohol had put my body in shock.

Discharged I felt like a new person. I got back to my room, enjoyed a deep hot bath and fresh clothes and applied make up.

I went straight to the bar. All the old faces were there, they all said, "Hi."

No one seemed that welcoming or bothered. I joined in conversations and was frustrated by the lack of attention I was getting. After four doubles, I left and headed back to my room. On the way I stopped by Valerie's office on the off chance.

She was in, and invited me in, "You look better. Have a seat. Would you like some juice?" She indicated to the orange juice on her desk.

"No its fine I said."

She took a step back and said dryly, "Vodka is normally taken with orange juice. Sarah, what the hell is it going to take? I can smell alcohol on your breath and you have been out of hospital for less than three hours!"

"I've lost my friends. They just don't seem to want to know me."

"Then they were not real friends, here drink this," she passed me a glass of OJ.

"I feel a tad lonely."

"You need to find a new crowd, people who don't expect you to be the entertainment, people who do not want a free ride, people who like you for being you."

"I don't really know who I am," I said, pathetically.

"Well, there is no time like the present to find out is there? Join in classes, be yourself, and you will make new friends, I promise you."

"OK."

"Come on Sarah. You have got to get with it, look, you have a body awareness dance lesson due in half an hour, go to your room, get your kit and join in."

I did. And slowly over the coming few weeks, I did not drink, I joined in classes, took extra dance and drama and even joined a poetry workshop, and I started to love what I was doing.

For the remainder of the term, I sailed through the fortnightly reviews and got straight A's. I started to indulge in extra classes and production and started to make new friends. By the third term, I had caught up to degree 2.1 standard and was heading for a first class honours degree. I retook two of the previous years' essays and improved my grades so my continued course work element lifted my grades.

I didn't go to the bar, but enjoyed writing essays long into the night. None of the old crowd ever came round or asked after me. I felt used given the alcohol and drugs that I had paid for to keep my parties going. I tried not to think about it. I did miss the closeness of skin to skin contact, the holding and the cuddling, so worked harder to take my mind off things.

One night on production I had to change a lamp. They are tricky things that are so delicate and it's best not to handle them hot, but the spotlight had blown and we had the interval to get it changed. I changed the bulb but the hot lamp shattered in my hand as I was climbing down the ladder. This resulted in another trip to casualty to get stitches.

I went alone to not cause disruption to the crew. I warned the nurse I may be HIV. She offered me a test. I took it, got the stitches and left. Within a fortnight I was told the test was negative. I was elated. After several years of fretting about having AIDS I finally knew there was little risk as the Uni nurse explained that some traces would have been found in the blood if I had contracted anything so severe. I vowed to myself that if God had been so generous that I would never again have sex like before. I would take no more chances. I would respect my body and enjoy the second chance.

The third term came and I was signed off performance review. I completed the four week teaching practice and got glowing reports. I was now in the last six weeks of term, and enjoying the education and learning.

Sarah's Story: **Temptation**

Then came the bad news from home that my Grandma had passed away. I loved her dearly. I was so upset that the only place I could think of going to was the bar. It was 11am and the bar was getting ready for opening at lunchtime.

I drank several doubles in one hit, and having been sober for a while they took affect quickly. I started to cry on Terrance's shoulder, who just kept filling my glass. The bar was empty and he and I were alone. He kissed me and I kissed him back he held me and I held him back. I suggested we go back to his room.

I craved closeness and physical contact. I wanted to be held, to feel love, so I started to tease him. I lifted my top to reveal a see through bra, and unzipped my Levi's so he could put his hand down my trousers and I rubbed against him teasing.

We carried on knocking back vodka shots and I let him touch me all over. At the height of his excitement I had him tied with long bar t-towels to the bed by the feet and hands and I danced naked around him, rubbing myself against him. He was hard and begging for me, but I teased some more. I was again enjoying the feeling of power and being in control. He then really started to beg me to do something, but I continued to tease until he was utterly embarrassed and I laughed at him for being weak. His embarrassment was making him a little annoyed and he tried to reason with me, I teased him all the more, touching him until he didn't know where he was.

With alcohol taking full effect, I untied his legs and lay naked between his legs, touching him and teasing until the alcohol made me fall asleep. About an hour later I came round. Terrance was awake and begging to be untied, I teased more until he was embarrassed again, but this time he was not enjoying it. He was cross and frustrated and angry, and I laughed at him and the more cross he got the more I teased. I knew that I was degrading him, the alcohol allowing me to be mean and whorish. I sat on his face just close enough to drive him mad, and pulled away. I got him hard and decided to slowly tease him with my tongue.

With one burst of anger, the ties came undone and in a flash he had me pinned down. “Get off, Terrance, get off me now,” I squealed feeling his weight

“Oh no Sarah, for hours you have had your way with me and it’s your turn now, you do not give what you can’t take.”

“Tez, get off me.”

He held my arms above my head and thrust into me, it hurt. He tried to kiss me I turned away. I tried to kick out but he bit into my breast.

“Tez no. I don’t want this, I don’t want to have sex with you, get off me you bastard.”

“Fuck you Sarah, you are a cock tease and you will get what’s coming to you and you will enjoy it.”

I tried to break loose, he was so much stronger and his grip on my arms tightened, the harder he gripped the more I wriggled. I tried to shut my legs on him, but he forced them open wedging himself on one leg so I couldn’t move.

“Will you fuck off me Tez you sick shit? I don’t want to have sex with you.”

“Oh but it’s OK for you to tease me, jack me off and laugh at me is it? Tough shit Sarah, you know you want it, you are gagging for it. It’s been a while, or so I heard, and you never had a real man. Though, from what I’ve heard, women are more your thing now. Well you can have a taste of real man Sarah to add another notch on your already well-notched bedpost.”

He carried on entering me forcefully, holding me tight, biting my neck and breasts and I could not move. His knee was wedged in one thigh and his hands pinned me down. I recoiled with every bite and lick but the more I struggled the more it hurt. He eventually finished and lay on me, breathing heavily, his sweat making me feel sick. He then used the ties that had bound him to bind me to the bed, first my arms then he tied my legs so I was spread eagled. He left the room.

I screamed out for him to come and untie me, to come and let me go, I screamed that he was a sick pervert. He came back and lay next to me.

“It’s only what you did to me Sarah. You should not give what you can’t take.”

He started to kiss me all over, breathing heavily, biting and rubbing. Every moment making me feel dirtier, more ashamed and sick. The more I struggled the more the ties hurt my wrists, they were too tight and, no matter how I twisted and turned, they would not come loose.

Aroused he entered me again, but this time I didn't move. I lay still, crying. When he finished he got dressed leaving me bare and exposed.

"You are one over-rated fuck Sarah. I reckon a corpse would have held more excitement."

He untied me and I crawled off the bed and got dressed. I left my underwear and just put on Levi's and my top. I ran for the door and out into the fresh air and back to my room. I stopped to throw up in the bush on the way. I looked at myself in the mirror and I looked a fright. There was blood on my lips. I went to the internal phone in the corridor and called Valerie. I begged her to come over.

"What is wrong Sarah? I have a departmental meeting about to start."

"I have been raped," I said. I heard Valerie take a sharp intake of breath.

"I'll be with you soon Sarah. Stay in your room."

Valerie came and I was almost hysterical, sobbing through snot and tears and unable to breathe. Valerie tried to calm me.

She said she would make tea and left the room. She was back a few moments later with sweet tea. She held me as I continued to sob.

It seemed like no time until I heard an ambulance turn up.

"Sarah, I will be with you, we need to get you checked." They wrapped a blanket around me, but I clung like a child to Valerie, still sobbing.

The hospital staff were gentle, but I was in a terrible state, I could not stop shaking and crying, but they got me into a gown eventually. They explained that they needed me to speak to a lady WPC who had appeared. Between sobs, I told her about what Terrance had done. I explained I was upset and that he invited me to his flat, then he wanted sex. I was too embarrassed to tell the truth. I was too embarrassed to detail my part to play.

They took samples from me internally and photographed the red marks on my wrist and feet, they photographed my cut lip and the bites, the marks from the ties that bound me and the bruising that was starting to appear on my thigh.

Valerie stayed with me until I was discharged and took me to get a pizza before taking me back to my room. It was close to midnight when we got back. She assured me she would be back at 8am.

I didn't sleep. I lay awake all night trying to figure out if I had been raped or if it was my fault. I knew I should have mentioned my part, but then I also knew I had said no. I had told him time and time again that I did not want to have sex with him and I pleaded with him to get off me, he made me have sex with him twice against my will and to me that was rape.

I also had to acknowledge that I had led him on and that I had gone overboard in my actions. I was confused. I was also not going to tell anything more than I had to. I was sick of men just taking me for granted and I was sick of sex, every time it taking more of me and leaving less of whom I wanted to be. I despised myself and the whole episode made me feel dirty and empty.

Valerie turned up at eight the next morning with coffee and croissants. She looked worried but we talked about the production of Swan Lake instead of what happened. At ten o'clock there was a knock on the door and Valerie invited the men in. The man turned out to be the College Principal accompanied by the lady WPC from the hospital.

With Valerie holding my hand, I repeated all that had happened. The WPC confirmed that sex had taken place according to the samples taken and fibres that were not from my clothes were also found. The fibres were of a woollen blue jumper, which is what I had said Terrance was wearing. The police were apparently in his apartment now taking samples from the bed and locating the ties and his clothes. They had confirmed my underwear had been found in his bin and that it was clear from his flat that intercourse had taken place. The photos of me were shown to the Principal. He also asked to see the bruises on my wrists and ankles, though not the bite marks or bruising. The pictures were evidence enough. He then left the room and the WPC took more pictures, the bruising now purple and blue and dramatic looking.

When everyone left, I went and sat next to Valerie. "Valerie, what is going on? This is freaking me out?"

"They arrested Terrance this morning Sarah on the charge of raping you. He has been removed from the Uni grounds. I understand that the Principal is going to suspend him until, well until I guess you decide what you are going to do."

I started to sob again and she just held me. "Valerie, can I have a bath now?"

"I think so Sarah, let me make a call and check."

Valerie went out to the phone booth and made the call, she came back and confirmed it was fine, but that the WPC wanted to come and see me straight after.

I had a bath feeling utterly ashamed of myself on every level. I put on a dressing gown and waited for the WPC who wanted more photos now the bruising was coming out. My wrists were blue as were my ankles and the bite marks were red and angry. The bruising to my thigh looked terrible and far worse than it felt. Not having much fat on me had made the bruises ten times worse than they were in reality and even I was shocked at how angry the bruising looked. It certainly looked worse than it was.

I learnt by mid-afternoon that Terrance had indeed been suspended. Instead of being relieved, I was shaken by the consequence of my actions, but now I couldn't stop them?

Valerie stayed with me that afternoon. As news got out, the bar clan came to see me with angry accusations of "What was I doing?" Some so-called friends accused me of behaving like a slut and what did I expect?

Every time it reduced me to more tears. Several of the old crowd had given statements, especially the guys about my flirtatious and teasing behaviour and indicated it was only a matter of time before someone returned the behaviour.

Valerie left at 8pm. Another call came, this time pointing out that Terrance would lose his job and career for my lies. They all knew the sex games I would play and would be supporting him and not me. One after one, the bar lot came to the room calling me a vicious cow, a liar and a manipulator. They all pointed out the consequences this would have professionally for him. I knew in my heart I needed to say something, but I couldn't. My head and heart were in conflict and all I knew was I that I had said no, and he should have stopped.

By 10pm I got in my car and drove to the chemist on the rota in the next town where I bought sleeping tablets and Paracetemol.

By 11pm I had swallowed the lot in the bath where I had decided to scrub myself with a scouring pad and bleach.

Apparently it was a first year that found me and called the ambulance. By 2am I was having my stomach pumped in hospital and at 4am Valerie was slapping my face calling me a selfish self obsessed cow and shaking me.

As I drifted in and out of consciousness, I secretly hoped to go back to the white lights that happened last time, to feel that peaceful place. It didn't come to me.

By 7am she was also in tears, apologising, saying I had frightened her. I was sorry too.

Valerie took me home to her apartment local to the Uni, where I stayed for the rest of the term. I concentrated on the second year exams and worked as hard as I could to get top grades. Valerie and I got on well and whilst I stayed in my room as much as possible working, she was very caring and kind.

Terrance resigned. I was sent firmly to 'Coventry' in so much as either anyone who was part of the loyal bar clan refused to speak to me, or would be utterly ruthless in what they said. As far as the Uni were concerned, if I wished to press charges I could. I chose not to. I signed a statement to say I wanted to leave it at that.

I asked what would happen with Terrance and was told that he had resigned and on his record there would be no details of the accusations as I had withdrawn my complaint. Whilst I could not forgive myself for my actions, I felt comforted to know he would still get work and his career would not be damaged.

I asked Valerie if I could give up on QTS as I wanted to finish at year three and leave. She made enquiries and I chose to focus on English and Psychology to replace missed units in removing the teaching practice for year three.

I was given a room in another campus at the end of the academic year. Given that I was leaving QTS and my focus was on other subjects I was better placed in the other campus at a sister college. Taking into consideration my welfare it seemed logical to move me. Valerie had also resigned as she had got her dream job teaching drama therapy in a prestigious hospital and whilst I was happy for her, I was sad she was leaving.

I applied for a summer job on reception at the new college which I got with board and breakfast included. I moved into my new room and set on creating a new start.

With the demons of the term behind me, I had a lot of work to do to replace missed credits in three modules. I secured special consent to be able to re-sit over summer due to the end of year circumstances. In addition, I had lots of reading to do for my replacement studies for year three. I had decided to live out so I needed to search for digs at the end of vacation. I was glad to be away from the campus that had brought so much trouble, but was looking forward to focusing on my English and Psychology and having a quiet studious year.

The reception desk was quiet with a handful of lecturers coming in and out and it was a case of just signing people in and out of the building. I absorbed myself in reading and had the odd chat with people as they came and went and built up good rapport with several academic staff.

I got on particularly well with a willowy curvaceous naturally blonde haired lady called Susan who wore the most amazing floating dresses and scarves. She was a lecturer in art history and psychology and loved the theatre and poetry. She was on a year's placement to give support to the new art history department.

Now: **Susannah**

Sarah told me that her notion of a Mother Figure originally came from her relationships with Jo and then Valerie.

Sarah explained that these people just took care of her when she felt she needed that female role model in her life, no matter what the circumstances. She explained to me that, in times of emotional crisis, these women have been the ones who were strong enough to pull her out of her mire and show her the way forward.

Sarah explained that after Valerie, there had been no one else in her life until Susannah. For twenty-five years she has not felt like she needed anyone.

When Sarah first got the call from Katie, it took her to a region of her psyche that she had blocked away. It made her realise that locking away things for a long time, whilst being expedient, had left many things unanswered and buried in her unconscious mind.

Recalling that past also put Sarah back into that place where she was forced to deal with it. However reliving the past also made Sarah weak emotionally. It made her realise how so many of the 'problems' or 'difficulties' she had faced related back to unanswered questions and unresolved feelings.

Maybe Sarah needed these answers for different reasons. Going back in time stirred many emotions for her. Sometimes Sarah found that, for days, she regressed to just how she was emotionally and psychologically back then. Sarah at times regained the emotional intelligence of a seventeen year old, with no direction, but simply with a craving for a mother's love or just a hug. Her episodes of extreme emotion and negative thought process left her vulnerable and out of her depth.

In such emotional crises, Sarah explained that she had previously attached herself to a strong woman. This time it was no different, Sarah had Susannah.

Unlike previous mother substitutes, Susannah was more practical and, instead of giving direction, had just given an ear.

There have been times that Sarah has confided that she wanted to run away from real life. Susannah made it clear that was not going to happen. Susannah maintained she could be a friend to Sarah, but the strain her problems had put on the friendship meant that a friendship would never be 'real'. There were times when Sarah demanded more from Susannah, but she explained she could not give that.

What Susannah had always done is repeat one message to Sarah.

"I am here and I care, and I will be here for as long as you need me." I have lost count of the amount of times Sarah has told me that Susannah has said that.

Maybe that's all Sarah needed to hear to be able to explore the past emotions and deal with them. Sarah didn't want or need professional help, it was a miracle she had seen the Doctor in the first place, but let's face it, the medical profession want to put everything in boxes and prescribe pills to deal with it.

And that is not the right way to treat everything.

The problem was, Sarah still had strong feelings going beyond those that can be explained this simply, and this is where Sarah tells me of her memory of the strongest relationship she ever had with a woman. The beautiful and loveliness of Susan.

Sarah's Story: **West End Girls**

Susan and I chatted every day as she signed in and out of reception. Sometime we would chat for a few minutes, but soon we began to spend half an hour chatting or more. We often made each other late. We had the same interests in the arts and the same sense of humour.

One morning Susan, rather shyly for her, asked, "I have some tickets for a mime show on at South Bank tonight, I have read good reviews, would you like to come with me?"

"Wow, yes, sure," I said, flattered she'd even asked.

"That's great Sarah; it's really great you will come, especially with such short notice. We would need to leave here at about 6ish, will that be OK?"

"Yes, that's fine, er, do you know the finish times so I can get back?"

"You're welcome to stay over Sarah, and come in with me in the morning. It will finish quite late. I live in Kensington so it's easy by cab or tube, but getting out into the suburbs is more difficult when it's late, and I would hate the thought of you on your own in the night."

"Thanks, and yes, I will crash at yours if it's OK."

We parted company and I spent the day looking forward to some real quality time with Susan that evening. She was intelligent, witty and really calm; her sheer presence relaxed me and made me feel open and receptive.

The evening was amazing, the performance excellent and afterwards we had dinner looking out onto the River Thames. The city lights and the buzz of her company made me almost giddy. We got back to her place and she had made me a bed in her spare room. Her apartment was utterly amazing with pictures of all the old films, prints of everything from the Wizard of Oz to My Fair Lady, posters of ballets and opera and some stunning art. It was a visual feast of magical fantasy.

We curled up on her sofa into the wee hours drinking red wine and munching pretzels. There was so much we had a shared interest in, we could have talked until the morning, but we were both tired so retired to our beds at 2am.

The following morning we both said what a wonderful night was and agreed to repeat it soon.

This was the start of twice weekly trips which ranged from popular West End shows, one off performances at South Bank, art exhibitions or just visiting the British Library. I would stay over and sometimes I would spend a weekend at hers while we planned our days out. The adventure was made more exciting with impromptu picnics and grabbing last minute deals on shows.

By midsummer we were close friends. Susan knew nothing of my past and it didn't matter. We had so much in common that there were always so many things to debate, discuss and muse over. There was nothing taboo that we didn't discuss.

We had been close for about a month when, whilst I was staying over, which was now commonplace, and as we snuggled under a sofa blanket watching one of my favourite films, Susan took my hand and held it. She snuggled into me and we were very close. She then leaned over to kiss me.

"Su, what are you doing Hun?" I said pulling away.

"Sarah, I thought you knew how I felt about you."

"Sorry?"

"I love you so much."

"I love you too but . . ."

"But not in that way?" She pulled back looking crestfallen, "I am so sorry Sarah, I just thought you felt the same, I thought we were getting on so well."

"We are."

"But not well enough?" she said.

My head raced. It took seconds that felt like minutes to find words. "I am sorry Su, I mean, are you . . . are you gay?"

She laughed, "I am bisexual Sarah. I sort of don't believe in name tags, it's more complicated or simpler for me than that."

"How? Why?" I asked.

She sighed, "Sarah, I just believe that the human body is a carcass. We are born into a physical sex, but our souls are sexless, which basically means we all have the power to fall in love with the spirit of the person, not the physical gender - does that make sense to you?"

It did, more than anything. "Yes, that makes perfect sense," I said.

Susan looked sad and let go of my hands and said, "Well, I love you Sarah, and I am sorry I mis-read the signs, but I thought you felt the same."

"I do. I mean, I do love you. It's just you're a girl." We laughed.

She said, "Well I was the last time I undressed Sarah! I didn't realise you didn't know how I felt, I am so sorry I have made you uncomfortable."

Susan took my hand again, noticing that the tension had lifted from my shoulders. "I'm sorry Sarah, forgive me?"

I then leant over and kissed her on the lips, "Nothing to forgive," I said.

She held me tightly and we began to kiss properly, slowly and with so much love, gentleness and respect, it was spine tingling. I loved Susan more than anyone I could think of, her brilliant mind, her love of art, her wicked wit and her softness of body and soul.

A while later she asked, "Will you sleep in my bed tonight Sarah, it would mean so much to me?"

I wanted to feel the closeness of her and I wanted to hold her, it was the closeness I secretly craved almost constantly. "I would love to," I said, and we went to her room.

Su undressed and I watched her move with grace and confidence. Her body was beautiful, curvy and her skin so radiant. She was not thin or fat, but looked as a healthy woman should with bumps and lumps. She climbed naked in between the sheets which were silk on cotton. I slipped off my jeans and top and climbed in beside her, leaving my underwear on. She snuggled up to me and kissed me again.

"Goodnight Sarah, sweet dreams," she held me close and I fell almost instantly asleep in her arms. It was the closeness I had craved for years; it was the being held and the skin to skin contact that was so reassuring and complete.

We can't have moved all night as we woke together still in each other's arms. She stroked my hair, kissed my head, and we talked about the stars and planets and how the planet seemed so tiny and, if that seemed tiny then we were just mere specks.

She finally said, "Thanks Sarah, it was lovely having you beside me."

"I liked it too . . ."

"Would you like to stay at mine for the rest of summer? When term starts, you were thinking of living out, so why not with me, here?"

"Can I think about it? I have lots of studying to do."

"Sure, I have lots of work too, so I am neither distraction nor help."

Then: A new kind of love

I decided to move in with Susan. It was the right thing to do on both counts. We would walk hand in hand and sometimes kiss in public, we would look into each other's eyes and finish each other's sentences, and at night we would hold each other and sleep in each other's arms.

For me, the physical closeness, the warmth and love was incredible. The way Susan made me feel so secure loved and grounded was something alien to me and I loved it and her. The physical side grew and we started to explore each other further. It was neither rushed nor intrusive.

I was nervous of the bedroom procedure. I had started to pretend to sleep because I was not sure how to react to her more intimate touch. I wasn't really sure what to do, and secondly, I still had awful flashbacks of having sex with men that reduced me to a shaking sweaty mess periodically. I wasn't sure I could bear to be touched intimately by anyone, even though, with Susan, it felt right.

I decided that the best option was to talk about it, so I bought champagne and oysters which I knew from the seafood bars we visited were a favourite. I wanted to be open with her, without me hurting her. My plans went downhill when I realised I did not know how to cook oysters so had to ask Susan to do them, which she thought was hilarious.

Whilst we were cooking I blurted it out, "Su, I am nervous, I mean, I want to be close to you, but, I mean I don't know what to do, really, you know, when you touch me, I, I mean, I like it, but I don't know what to do. Oh God, Su this sounds hilariously stupid, I am so sorry, I just had to talk to you about it."

She smiled at me and gave me a hug, "You have slept with blokes before right?"

"Well, I have had sex, but it meant nothing, and I mean nothing. No feeling and certainly no fireworks or boom bands. In fact I just felt used and empty."

"Crap bloke sex hey?" she laughed. "Been there done that, bought the T-shirt and am still waiting for the refund. Sarah, have you ever made love?"

I thought about it. Clearly for too long.

"If you are having to think about it, then the answer's no, Sarah."

"I don't know, I have had sex, but it meant nothing, I felt nothing physically really, it was just an act, so what does that mean?"

"It means you have had bad bloke sex, which is meaningless and pointless. It's a bloke act that they get off on, leaving you feeling empty and used."

That feeling rang all the bells and ticked all the boxes.

"Yup, you're right, so how do I change that?"

"You stop worrying about it. Stop thinking about it and you simply follow what feels right, with someone you have feelings for. You do what feels good and you reject what doesn't."

She hugged me. "You are so innocent Sarah, it's so sweet."

I nearly choked. That was one word that certainly was not appropriate.

"Sarah, stop fretting and add the white wine to the oysters before they frazzle." Susan moved away and I felt confused still.

The oysters were amazing and I could have eaten more, we had them with artichoke which we dipped in homemade mayo that Su made. After eating, we sipped champagne and as we both started to feel woozy we went to bed, together, with our last glasses of champagne. I was relaxed and Su gave me a massage which was divine. She softly touched me and I responded to her touch. Her touch felt so right, so gentle. The kisses in between felt so natural.

I had never had an orgasm before. I had never spoken about it or discussed it and I certainly didn't want to know details. I had assumed this could only be something that a man could do by entering me, but Su managed this by touch alone. I held her so tightly and she stroked my head until I fell asleep in her arms.

I felt so utterly together with her like we were one being, and after time, I was able to pleasure her in the same way.

I liked the fact there was no penetration, there was nothing that felt aggressive or degrading or shameful. I loved the softness of the female body and how the touch was physical but somehow fed by the sensation of the mind as well.

In time, my confidence grew with her and we were soon having the best of times, both in and out of the bedroom. We travelled to Uni every day together and returned home together, this often meant one of us working in the library around the other schedules but it was fine. In the evenings we worked on our studies; we cooked fabulous food and drank great wine, and slept together every night. Holding her and waking up with her was the most intense but most natural thing in the world.

My eating disorders vanished into thin air, I had put on weight and it felt fine. I felt happy with my body and Susan reassured me I was lovely. I learnt from touching her body, that bumps and lumps are fine. In fact they are sensuous and for the first time I truly appreciated that bodies are not meant to be bony and angular, but soft and sensual, warm and inviting. There was no need to feel ashamed about a little weight, as making love was not so much about the physical touch. It was nothing unless the mind was totally engaged too. It was essential to have a meeting of minds and entwining of souls that almost momentarily become one, as well as the physical joining that made making love special. When emotionally you are this connected, and the touch is right, that's when the 'boom bands' play.

I didn't have any other friends; I didn't need anyone but Su. It was clear she felt the same. We respected each other's space when working, could talk about anything and supported each other through thick and thin during the year. I had never felt so emotionally stable and balanced. The emotionally starved part of me that used to run a rage through me had subsided, the closeness of Susan keeping the monster within me at bay. As the year came to a close and finals were sat, I knew the relationship was also coming to an end. I wanted to take a year doing a specialist theatre course and Su wanted to go to Germany to continue her PhD whilst being a mentor.

The difference in future plans started to form in both of our minds and we discussed having to go our separate ways. We knew each other well enough to know we would not get back together.

From the day Susan confirmed her flight and put the apartment on the market to rent, the emotions running between us became unbearable. We cried we hugged and we savoured every moment together. I felt like my heart was breaking and was waiting for a miracle to stop this cruel separation.

The night before we held each other for the last time, I helped her pack.

"Sarah, you can have this, call it a token of my love."

We dissolved into laughter as she produced the frying pan-come-wok she had bought after my oyster cooking debacle.

"Really Susan," I laughed. "You have it, you know cooking is more your forté."

She kissed me on the cheek. "One day you will cook with this wok and it will be for someone you love. I mean really love, who you will spend the rest of your life with."

We held each other, kissing all night. Secretly hoping the sun would not rise the next morning.

The next day when she left, I was inconsolable. I sat by the lake in the park crying and praying she would come back. I waited for several hours, watching every plane go over head, wondering which one she was on.

Once dark, I went back to my new studio flat that I had taken on a four week rental, at hideous cost, and felt the loneliest I had ever felt. My heart was breaking and the pain of wanting and needing was unimaginable. It tore at me every moment of the day. I contemplated giving up my course to be with her, but I knew that she would not want that.

She didn't call. We had agreed not to call each other, but I hoped she would. I did not know her number, so I was reliant on her calling me.

I waited for the post every day, but other than the card which spoke of how much she loved me and missed me, I heard nothing. I prepared to start my drama course, which having graduated with a 2.1 I had been instantly accepted on. I had two weeks left in the studio and then I would take digs in a shared house in North London.

It was a new chapter and I was intensely excited about taking my learning further. I had a goal and I was determined to make it happen. I had come so far in the last year and the old me had gone forever.

Susan had taught me how to find love, how to be in love and how to make love. She taught me about respecting myself and making a stand and how to move on. I was not going to let her or myself down as I embarked on the start of the future, with a happy and optimistic heart.

Now: **Susannah**

Sarah could never explain the feelings for Susannah... She could never understand at the time if she was in love with her or the fantasy of her as a mother figure.

Was it possible the same type of essence could incarnate in two different people? Perhaps some kind of karmic resonance attracts us to symbiotically feed from those who can provide just the right soul nourishment.

The point Susannah came into Sarah's life coincided with the first call from Katie. Emotions that had been buried for over twenty years came flooding to the surface, and the only person Sarah felt she could talk to was Susannah.

The emotions of how she felt for her, coupled with the emotions from her past flooded back and triggered another spell of bulimia.

As the months went by, the more Sarah confided in Susannah and the more attached and dependent she became, her feelings changed from seeing her as a friend to seeing her as a Mother Figure.

Susannah's support of Sarah has always exceeded Sarah's expectations and her kindness has been humbling. However, this relationship was terribly one-sided and at some point Sarah knew it would have to end.

Susannah explained to Sarah that she would always as someone who had made a monumental change on her outlook. She would always be someone who had has helped her address the history she had locked away.

Sarah also knew a day would come when she would have to say goodbye. She lived for a long time in fear that this day would come, unsure of how she would cope.

Sarah's Decision

After enrolling on her drama course Sarah felt she had a new aim.

Sarah instantly felt that the people on the course were not real. Sarah felt like the red hat amongst a sea of blue hats. She was different. She was not pretentious, Sarah wasn't into 'me, me, me" and was not into the body perfection that seemingly went with the dramatic persona. Sarah's peers were mostly 'eating disorder personified', definitely a world in which Sarah did not want to return. It was as though some of her peers were in the adolescent phase Sarah was in only five years before. Sarah felt somehow older and more mature.

Sarah describes this day as being like being the odd one out in the clones, beautiful teeth and size two-six bodies, wearing minimal clothing, starving or puking, blonde or more like bottle blond hairdos. There were bodies with lifts, tucks, sucked or bleached, nose jobs, boob jobs and Botox, all at twenty-five or less. It seemed fake, false and hopeless. The empty and pointless conversation matched well and Sarah just could not be bothered.

Sarah didn't want to go back to this. She was lonely. She didn't like it. She felt so alone it hurt.

Sarah needed a job. She called the college up and spoke to head of security and begged for her job back part time. They were happy to have her. Sarah took every shift on offer outside of studies and met a gentleman who was older but who had a deep spiritual side.

By the third week of the course, Sarah knew this life was not for her. She could not bear the thought of going into one more practical classes, she doubted anyone would notice if she were there or not anyway.

The following day Sarah walked into class. Sarah describes the moment like an outer body experience. She could see what everyone was doing, like it was unreal. She saw the scene for what it was. It was nothing. It was a group of people dressed in black pretending. Egos on a stick, with performance on their brains. There was no reality or depth. Sarah had to leave.

Sarah describers the decision making moment like a brighter light bulb been turned on so you can now clearly see in the shadows and see something for what it is, allowing you to reject it. As she surveyed the scene before her, she decided she would never return. Sarah took in the moment and whispered goodbye under her breath.

Back at the studio flat with just a day left, Sarah packed everything up in the back pack. The only thing she could not fit in was the frying pan come wok that Susan had given her. Sarah toyed with leaving it, but as she was locking the door she decided it should stay with her and Sarah smiled as she recalled her trying to cook the oysters.

Sarah didn't have anywhere to go. She planned to take a B&B somewhere and think about what happens next. She had no other plans. She contemplated heading for the train station to go back home to her family.

Sarah had only one commitment in her life at this point in time. She had agreed to meet the kindest man on earth who she had got to know from working on reception. Sarah said she would feel bad not turning up and as she was due to met at 8pm she was determined to spend the evening with him.

Sarah arrived at the bus stop by the green at 8pm where they had agreed and waited. She did not look ideal date material with her backpack and frying pan. Buses came and went, as did 9pm and not yet a peek. Something was wrong. It must have been. Sarah felt a bit silly, and having never gone on a date before now realised what the term "stood up" meant.

At 9.45pm, Sarah started to walk to another bus stop to take her into the town. Then she heard a voice, "Sarah, please wait, I am sorry."

She watched as he approached her. "I am sorry. I was with my Mother. She just died."

Sarah reached out and held him, her arms wrapped in his. A tight embrace full of love and full of future. She opened her eyes. She saw the kindness and love shining back in his eyes.

They held each other tight for a long time. As Sarah opened her eyes she realised she was holding the frying pan in one hand.

He said, "You're not going to bash me with that, are you?" Sarah laughed and they headed off, hand in hand.

Afterword

Appreciating the Angels has saved Sarah, time and time again!

I was privileged that Sarah shared her story with me. With my own beliefs in place, I know everything happens I believe that everything happens for a reason, even though we may not understand it or realise it at that juncture in time. I also believe that there is no such thing as a chance meeting.

I look back at Sarah's life and I see people who hurt her. I see people that cared for her. I see people she did not care for even though they tried to help or care for her.

For all of us there are people we have loved, who have not been able to love us back. There are people who have loved us and we have not given them any time or love in return. And, whilst we have suffered at the hands of other people, we have also made people suffer because of our actions.

We shouldn't feel regret, nor should we feel guilt. For whatever the universal reason; these things were meant to be.

I met a lady about ten years ago at a cemetery. She cried at the grave of her son who was three when he died. This lady was there every single day for months. I never spoke to her, but I prayed for her. I could not contemplate why a 'god' could allow so much hurt to happen and so much pain to people who just did not seem to deserve it.

Then suddenly, the jigsaw pieces fell into place for me. I realised that the length of our life here on earth is in our eternal life, the shortest of times. We are given a physical body and live on earth where time is slowed down. It is nothing by comparison to the eternal life of our spirit and our soul as a whole.

It's just a flash in the pan.

We are here to learn, to make us better souls, to progress on astral planes where we work towards greatness and a better light so as to become one whole of something greater and more divine. Be that God, Jehovah, Allah or the Source. It is ultimately all the same.

When you start to accept the bigger universal picture, you realise that we all have our task while we are here and we have to deal with things the best we can.

Mistakes we make give us time to reflect and learn. We meet people to challenge us, to enhance us, to hurt us and to inspire our hearts. It's part of a plan that our little conscious minds can't always appreciate, though we are the ones that pre chose our earthly mission.

What I do know for sure, is that there are higher forms of being. On the astral plane and walking alongside us, they are our Angels and they will help us, if we only ask for guidance.

Is a friend for a reason, season or lifetime?'

Well maybe we chose the meeting and already knew the answer and the purpose of that other soul in our life.

Sarah chose to not deal with things for twenty years, hiding from emotion, hiding from feeling and struggling to be whom she wanted to be. Susannah allowed her to reopen doors and work through the pain she had boxed away.

Sarah played the main part in this story, but what happened to the others?

I began my research, with Sarah's permission, and we discovered that indeed the universe had continued to illustrate the impact each character played in the individual journeys.

Jo. Well Jo used her drama to become a drama therapist. She works with self-harming teens with eating disorders. Sammy, her daughter, was anorexic when Sarah met her, but no one realised she was also self-harming. In meeting Jo and so raising her awareness, she was able to help Sammy. Sammy had never heard of laxative abuse until hearing Jo discuss this with Sarah, to her shame this gave her the idea, the idea in turn which lead to her having heart failure. She lived. Jo can tell you that story. But because of Sarah's meeting, her life changed course dramatically.

Ruthie was a talented actress, singer and songwriter. The day she saw Sarah's scars she realised that human emotion is so strong it can kill our very being. Her songs tell her tale as she is now a successful singer songwriter who, anonymously, mentions Sarah in her inspiration. Ruthie lost touch with Sarah but they met years later. She explained that she fell in love with Sarah, and her vulnerability. This led to her break up with Jo. Sarah never knew. Her story is all about unrequited love and the pain of being openly gay. It's heartbreaking and inspirational. She dedicates her life to working within the gay community in helping teens deal with coming out. Her story is fascinating. She is a truly inspirational lady.

Terrance lost his job. His weak marriage did not survive his homecoming. It had been on the rocks a while as living away put pressure on a loveless marriage. His confidence shattered, his trust in women destroyed he went home a broken man. That he told his wife the truth is a credit to him, but she left anyway. She took his children with her. He was heartbroken and committed suicide a year later.

Paul did not think again about the sexual attack on a fourteen year old. He raped plenty of other girls a similar age and went on to have a violent relationship with a woman who he beat and raped leading to the sum of six children. After many years of abuse and a near-death beating of her, she found he had abused her eldest daughter. She stood tall in the magistrate's court and saw him sent down. Her life began again and the children are now with her new partner in Wales living a more peaceful life. He is still inside serving his sentence. His story is one of rage. His rage stems from his own childhood in which he himself was abused. His story is full of sadness, anger and hate.

Bill died. He died in JJ's arms six months after getting the all clear. In those six months, JJ had the best of times followed by the worst of times. JJ coped. Sarah knew she could and would. JJ dedicated her life to her children who are all now married and living close by in the glen. Ted and Patricia became part of her family after Sarah left. Sarah had brought the two families together in her time and this bond lasted. Bill's passing bought new life to Ted who walked the girls to school and Patricia had a family to cook and care for. Despite the tragedy, JJ's story is heart-warming and hopeful. Her children are balanced adults now, loving and full of love and very happy memories of their father. Sarah was glad she had brought the two families together. She knew this time cemented something that affected and changed lives forever. Patricia died last year. Charlie, Emma and Tess all married now with their own children gave her a spectacular send off. Her diaries were found left to JJ a few months later. Her story spanning eighty years of devotion to those nearest and dearest, an amazing read of one terrific lady.

Jane and Mark split over Sarah. She was apparently the last straw for Jane who was aware of Mark's frequent indiscretions. Jane's story mentions Sarah and places her in a pivotal role as she cared for Sarah as a young screwed up girl. She could see it, and hated Mark for taking advantage. Jane was raped as a teen, her story is compelling, but explains why she put up with Mark for so long time as he was her first true love. Over time, she despised him until it had to end.

Mark up and left and the Lord gave him a large hotel in some other area he owned and was influential. Mark's single status gave him sexual freedom, in which he, in his fifties remains single and the playboy. His story is about the woman and fast cars, there is little spirituality but great sex!

The Lord died in hospital a year after Sarah met him. Sarah heard he died of bowel cancer and it was rumoured his partner of twenty years was a transvestite homosexual called Philippe.

Susan met the love of her life and is now married and her partner had their baby two years ago. Chloe is a doting mother and girlfriend. Their story is rich with passion and true love. It's gentle and humbling.

Acknowledgements

I would like to acknowledge angels who brought Sarah into my life, allowed me to share her story and in doing so helped me recognise the angels who are walking alongside me and whom are manifesting themselves as:

My Husband and Father to my child, Colin. The most loving, most understanding of souls who is my best friend and the most amazing father to Little D. An Angel of immeasurable love.

Lizzi Vandorpe author of The Blessings Book – for everything, for her encouragement, her patience, understanding and perseverance with me to finally get this book into print. An Angel with divine timing!

Tom, aka The Bookwright, for believing in me and mentoring me through the writing stages. A technical Angel with an "App for that!"

Penny Power, founder of Ecademy for one day telling me that "Being YOU is ENOUGH" and therefore giving me the confidence to publish under my name. An Angel with impeccable timing!

Sarah, for sharing her story with me and thus showing us how we can all be Angels to each other.

The images in parts of this book are from the Crystals of the Divine Reality from Kryon School in Germany. I/We thank them for granting permission to use them.

Reviews

This book was so powerful to read I had to stand up while reading it. I was on a flight to Chicago and I found it so moving, so honest, so real, and so sad that I went to the back of the aeroplane crying my eyes out. I have led a sheltered life, I have never knowingly come into contact with anyone who has experienced the challenges Sarah had and survived such pain. You have given me an education and the ability to me more empathetic and understanding when people appear to be destructive, yet it is them-self they are trying to destroy. I am proud to have been this close to Sarah through her story. Congratulations on such a compelling book.

Penny Power – Founder of Ecademy

I've never read anything like this, thank heaven for it's publication. With brutal honesty Sarah conveys the truth about her teenage and student life. Parts of which I'm sure many will relate to on one level or another. This is a lesson in forgiveness and letting go.

Appreciating Angels has had a profound effect on me, drawing up emotions and memories. It has simultaneously brought a lump to my throat and filled my heart to overflowing. This book will reach many people – parents, daughters, sons, friends – listen and watch those around you who may be crying out for warmth, a hug and understanding – we can all learn to be Angels to one another as Sarah's Story so beautifully shows us.

Jackie Walker, Co-Founder Ugli Mediation